HEATING AIR CONDITIONING
FOR ASE TEST A7

2003 Edition

First Printing

D0899604

James R. Reese, SAE
Manager, Service Trade Editorial

EDITORIAL DEVELOPMENT

Senior Editors
Warren Schildknecht, SAE
Michael A. Zimmerman, ASE
Richard C. Grunz, ASE
Richard G. Glover, SAE
Jim Jackovatz
Scott Hansen, ASE

Associate Editor
Ron Lathrop

Technical Editors
Eric Rogowski, ASE
Pieter Johan Dijkstra
Keith Grainger
Richard H. Sparkes, ASE
Jeff Finamore
Anthony W. Dutton
Uche-Uwa Ogu
Daniel G. Paalanen, ASE

EDITORIAL PRODUCTION
Susan J. Verhelst, Coordinator
Catherine Starzyk
Julie Andrews
Elaine Finamore
Michele L. Hawley
Sheri Aquisto

Authorized Distributor

For Information On MOTOR Products Call
1-800-4A-MOTOR (1-800-426-6867)

Information Procurement Specialist
Holly Wright

Office Manager
Vita M. Green

BOOK PRODUCTION

Director of Technology
Robert Jaramillo

Manager, Database Systems
Steven J. Hollowell, CNA

Manager, Product Development/Technical Support
Tina Wrubel

Production Manager
Rosanne Ahee

Production Group
Janet Artman
Frank Jannaro
Christopher Mallory
Hilarie McMullen
Jonathan Pinfield-Wells

Manager, Production Services
Donna Kijek

MOTOR
INFORMATION SYSTEMS

MOTOR is a trademark of Hearst Business Publishing, Inc.

Published by Motor Information Systems, a division of Hearst Business Publishing, Inc. A Unit Of The Hearst Corporation

5600 Crooks Road, Troy, MI 48098

Printed in the U.S.A.

Victor F. Ganzi
President & Chief Executive Officer

Frank A. Bennack, Jr.
Vice Chairman

William M. Wright
Executive Vice President & Deputy Group Head, Hearst Business Media

Robert D. Wilbanks
Vice President & Group Controller, Hearst Business Media

Richard B. Laimbeer
Publisher, Motor Manuals

George R. Hearst, Jr.
Chairman

Richard P. Malloch
President & Group Head Hearst Business Media

William K. Baker
Vice President & General Manager, Hearst Business Media

Kevin F. Carr
President, Motor Information Systems

Marian A. Maasshoff
Director of Product Development

Heating and Air-Conditioning Test
FOR ASE TEST A7

Contents

Chapter One

AIR-CONDITIONING (A/C) SYSTEM DIAGNOSIS, TESTING, AND SERVICE

Air-Conditioning (A/C) diagnosis begins with a preliminary inspection and an evaluation of system performance. Although there is a variety of A/C systems, preliminary inspection procedures are similar for all designs.

PRELIMINARY INSPECTION AND DIAGNOSIS

During a preliminary inspection, system components should be visually checked for proper mounting and signs of damage, modification, or oil leakage. Then, the level of performance is evaluated while testing the operation of the system.

VISUAL CHECK

Examine A/C components for:

- Drive belt deterioration, damage, or incorrect tension
- Loose compressor mounts or brackets and worn bushings
- Jammed or warped clutch hub, or pulley damage
- Loose or damaged compressor clutch wiring or connectors
- Blown or missing fuses or circuit breakers
- Leaking hoses, lines, and fittings
- Blocked or damaged condenser and evaporator fins

If the system passes a visual inspection, switch the A/C on and listen for unusual noises. If any of the visual checks reveal potential problems, correct the concern and then proceed to the performance tests.

Unusual Operating Noises

To diagnose a malfunctioning A/C system by sound, listen for:

- Grinding noise, or roughness when the compressor clutch is engaged—defective clutch bearing

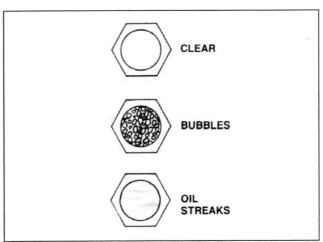

Fig. 1-1. *A sight glass provides a visual quick check of refrigerant condition.*

- Heavy knocking sound at the compressor—internal damage
- Clicking at the compressor—internal wear
- Squeal, rubbing noise, accompanied by blower motor vibration, often increasing with fan speed—defective bushings at the blower motor armature shaft
- Squeal upon compressor engagement—defective drive belt
- Thumps, whines, bangs—system blockage or incorrect system pressures
- Honking noise—low refrigerant level

Sight Glass Diagnosis

Some of the **Thermostatic Expansion Valve (TXV)** systems utilize a sight glass to allow for a visual check of the presence of refrigerant, figure 1-1. Sight glass location varies by system design. It may be located in the liquid line between the receiver-drier and the TXV, figure 1-2, or as an integral part of the receiver-drier assembly. The sight glass is always located on the

---

Thermostatic Expansion Valve (TXV): An expansion device that removes pressure from the refrigerant as it flows into the evaporator and also varies the refrigerant flow rate in relation to evaporator temperature.

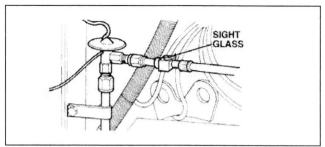

Fig. 1-2. *Sight glass location varies between systems, but is always on the high-side.*

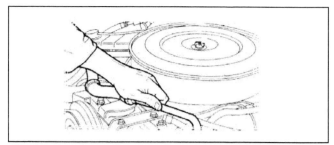

Fig. 1-3. *Exercise caution when diagnosing by touch because A/C components can be extremely hot or cold.*

high-side of the system. The type of refrigerant used in the A/C system determines how sight glass readings are evaluated.

Refrigerant-12 (R-12) Sight Glass

Because refrigerant is colorless, the sight glass should be clear. However, it is possible for an empty system to look clear. Looking into the sight glass of an empty system is like looking through an empty glass container. Other signs of an empty system include oil droplets or streaks on the glass.

A low refrigerant level, which allows vapor to enter the system through the pickup tube in the receiver-drier, is indicated by bubbles in the sight glass. As the system loses more refrigerant and takes in more vapor, the bubbles start to look like foam, and oil streaks may form across the glass. Recharge the system.

If refrigerant in the sight glass is a red or yellow color, the system contains leak-detecting dye. As long as the leaks have been repaired and the system is charged to specifications, no service is required.

Refrigerant-134a (R-134a) Sight Glass

Very few R-134a systems use a sight glass. If one is present, certain conditions must be met to get an accurate reading from the sight glass. Typically, a sight glass check is made when:

- Ambient temperature is below 95°F (35°C)
- Humidity is below 70 percent
- Engine speed is at 1,500 rpm
- The A/C switch is on
- Airflow is set to recirculate
- The blower fan is on high
- The temperature control is at the coldest position
- System high-side pressure is below 240 psi (1,670 kPa)

It is normal to see an almost transparent flow of bubbles that disappear at high throttle in an R-134a sight glass. If there are no bubbles, there is too much refrigerant in the system. A constant flow of bubbles, which can be transparent or frothy, indicates a low refrigerant level.

A faint foggy appearance indicates a very low refrigerant level. To repair, add refrigerant as needed.

If the sight glass is heavily fogged, the system may be contaminated by the wrong type of compressor lubricant. Mineral oil, as used in an R-12 system, reacts with R-134a, causing the foggy appearance and resulting in system damage. Repairs can range from a system flush and recharge to replacing the entire system.

Insight:
Never diagnose an R-134a system based on sight glass appearance only. It is much less reliable than the R-12 version.

Smells and Temperatures

If condensation cannot drain from the evaporator, the water stagnates, bacteria grows in the water, and a foul odor results. The blower sends air through the evaporator into the passenger compartment and the air becomes contaminated with this smell. Clean the evaporator assembly and repair the evaporator case or drain tube so the condensation can drain.

Insight:
There are several OEM Technical Service Bulletins (TSBs) available to aid in diagnosing and repairing evaporator odor issues.

A number of faults can be discovered by touching system parts. High-side components are normally warm or hot to the touch, while **low-side** components are cool or cold. When diagnosing the system by touch, use

---

High-Side: The portion of the A/C system in which the refrigerant is under high pressure and at high temperature. It includes the compressor outlet, condenser, receiver-drier, and expansion device inlet.

Low-Side: The portion of the A/C system in which the refrigerant is under low pressure and at low temperature. It includes the expansion device outlet, evaporator, accumulator, and compressor inlet.

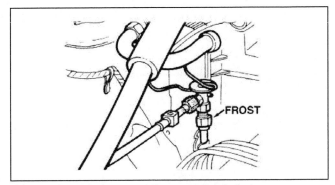

Fig. 1-4. *Frost forming on certain components indicates a malfunction.*

caution; move the back of your hand near the object, and touch it only if it does not seem extremely hot or cold, figure 1-3. Diagnose by touch as follows:

1. Check for frost on the outside of components, figure 1-4. Frost on the following parts indicates the problems listed:

   • Evaporator outlet could indicate a malfunctioning thermostatic switch
   • Expansion valve stuck shut or clogged with ice
   • Receiver-drier is restricted in the drier pickup tube or **desiccant** sleeve

2. Check the outlet line from the evaporator. It should be cool. If it is warm, the problem may be:

   • Little or no refrigerant in the system
   • No refrigerant pressure
   • The control system not allowing refrigerant release into the evaporator

3. On a TXV system, check the receiver-drier. It should be warm. On an orifice-tube system, the accumulator should be cool or cold.

4. Feel the temperature of the line leading from the condenser to the expansion device. It should be between very warm and hot. If it is cold, there may be a restriction in the high-side.

5. Check that the evaporator outlet is the same temperature as or colder than the inlet. If not, check system pressures and refrigerant level.

6. Check the compressor cylinder head. If it is hot or the paint has burned off, the compressor outlet valve may be broken.

SYSTEM PERFORMANCE TESTING

System performance testing, which involves operating the system and evaluating its output, varies by system design. The first step is to determine what type of system is used.

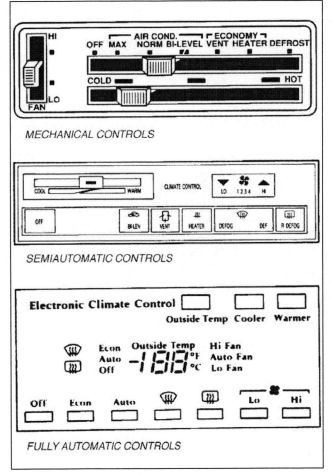

Fig. 1-5. *Typical A/C control heads.*

Identifying the Type of System

Some compressors run whenever the A/C is on, while others cycle on and off. Compressors that run continuously are variable displacement units that respond to crankcase suction-pressure differential. Systems in which the compressor cycles on and off are referred to as Cycling Clutch Orifice Tube (CCOT) systems.

Another way to identify a system is by the controls, which may be mechanical, semiautomatic, or fully automatic, figure 1-5. Mechanical systems use hand-operated slide switches or rotary switches. Semiautomatic systems generally use a lever and cable assembly to regulate temperature settings and push-button switches for the other control features. Fully automatic systems often have digital temperature readouts and setting features.

An A/C system can also be identified by the refrigerant control or expansion device used in the system.

Desiccant: A chemical agent in the receiver-drier of an A/C system, used to remove moisture.

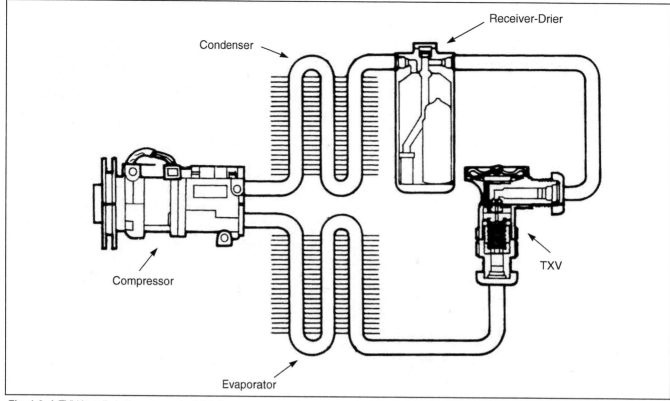

Fig. 1-6. *A TXV installs in the evaporator inlet line.*

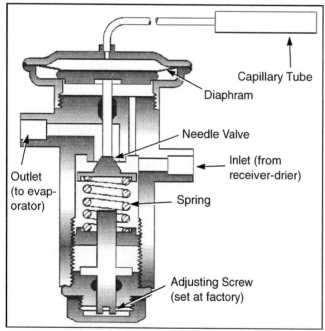

Fig. 1-7. *This type of TXV resembles a thermostat in the engine cooling system*

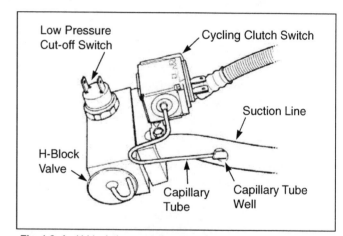

Fig. 1-8. *An H-block thermostatic expansion valve with a capillary tube.*

Expansion Devices

There are three types of expansion devices:

- Thermostatic expansion valve
- Fixed-orifice **expansion tube**
- **Variable-orifice expansion tube**

Expansion Tube: Also known as a fixed-orifice tube, this expansion device removes pressure from the refrigerant as it flows into the evaporator, but does not vary the flow rate.

Variable Orifice Expansion Tube: A type of expansion tube that varies the refrigerant flow rate to compensate for changes in compressor ouput.

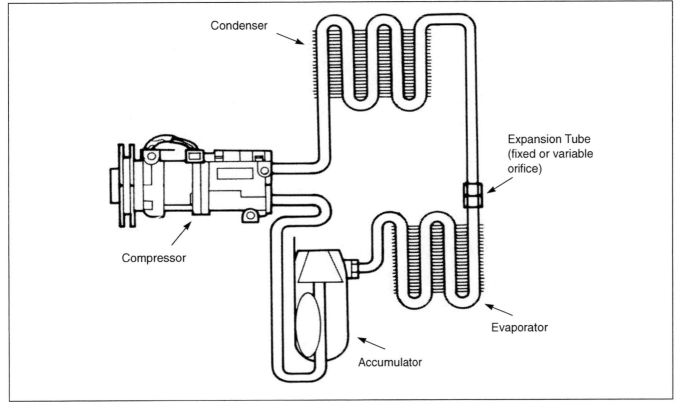

Fig. 1-9. *Fixed and variable orifice expansion tubes are located in the inlet line to the evaporator.*

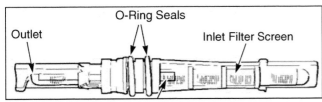

Fig. 1-10. *The fixed orifice expansion tube.*

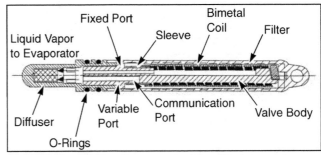

Fig. 1-11. *The variable orifice expansion tube offers increased performance at lower speeds.*

TXV Designs

Systems using a TXV are set up as shown in figure 1-6. There are two basic thermostatic expansion valve designs. One TXV design, which resembles the thermostat in the engine cooling system, is located in the evaporator inlet line, figure 1-7. The second TXV design has the valve encased in a thermostatic block valve or H-valve that installs on the inlet line to the evaporator. Regardless of design, a TXV may be mounted either in the engine compartment or on the evaporator case. In some systems, a capillary tube leads from the TXV to the evaporator to sense temperature, figure 1-8. The TXV inlet line, which is smaller than the outlet line, is warmer than the outlet during operation.

Cycling Clutch Orifice Tube (CCOT)

To visually identify a CCOT system, look for an accumulator in the line between the evaporator to the com-

pressor. Also, there is no receiver-drier in the line between the condenser and evaporator on an expansion tube system, figure 1-9.

Fixed Orifice Expansion Tube

The fixed orifice expansion tube, which separates the high and low-pressure sides of the system, is contained in the inlet line to the evaporator. Typically, the expansion tube is either part of the hose leading to the evaporator or a separate part fitted inside the hose. The size of the fixed orifice is a compromise between system performance at idle and highway speeds, figure 1-10.

Variable Orifice Expansion Tube

The variable orifice expansion tube uses system pres-

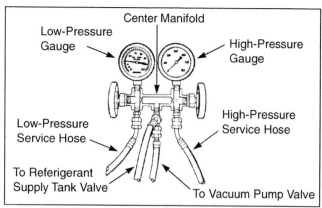

Fig. 1-12. A manifold gauge set monitors high and low-side pressures.

sure and refrigerant flow to move a metering piston in the sleeve, figure 1-11. When idling at high ambient temperatures, the piston shifts to a smaller metering area. This compensates for the reduced compressor output and increases the cooling performance.

Older Systems

There were other types of refrigerant control systems built in years past. A few of the systems were:

- Suction Throttling Valve (STV)
- Pilot Operated Absolute Pressure Valve (POA)
- Evaporator Pressure (EVP) Regulator

With the phase-out of R-12 refrigerant few of these systems are serviced today. For more information on these systems consult the applicable service manual.

Performance Test

A performance test checks how well the system operates in all the driver selected modes. To conduct the performance test:

1. Make sure the shop area is adequately ventilated before running the engine.
2. With the A/C system operating at the maximum (MAX) setting, verify that all of the plenum air is directed through the evaporator.
3. Install a thermometer in a panel outlet or vent grille.
4. With the A/C set to MAX and the blower fan on high speed, close all the vehicle windows and doors.
5. Allow the engine to run at idle for 10 minutes.
6. Increase engine speed to between 1500 and 2000 rpm and check output temperature. Temperature should be in the 35 to 40°F (2 to 7° C) range.

If the system is not performing satisfactorily, use a manifold gauge set to check system pressures, figure 1-12.

MANIFOLD GAUGE TESTING

Until recently, all automotive A/C systems operated with R-12. Because R-12 is a **Chlorofluorocarbon** (CFC), it is being phased out and is no longer produced. All newer automotive A/C systems are designed to operate with R-134a. Although there are other refrigerant blends available from the aftermarket, these two (R-12 and R-134a) are the only ones approved by the vehicle man-

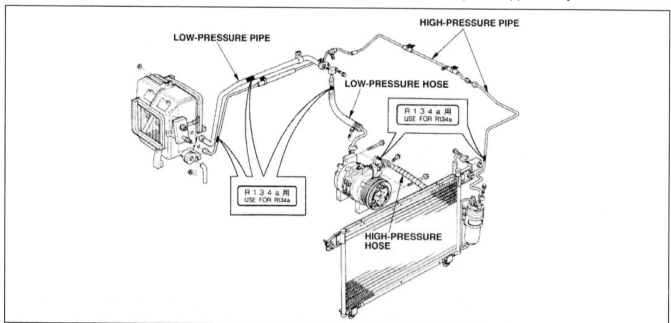

Fig. 1-13. Components designed to operate with R-134a are labeled accordingly.

Chlorofluorocarbon (CFC): A chemical compound containing chlorine, fluorine, and carbon. When released into the atmosphere, the chlorine atoms detach from the CFC molecules causing a chemical reaction that turns ozone molecules into oxygen. Oxygen does not filter ultraviolet light as ozone does. Refrigerant-12 (CCl2F2) is a CFC.

ufacturers. Also, the two refrigerants are incompatible, so separate sets of gauges, tools, and supplies are required for each.

Identifying R-12 and R-134a Systems

In a typical R-134a system, each major component—the condenser, compressor, evaporator, pressure switch, expansion valve, and receiver-drier—has a label on it stating that it is designed for use with R-134a, figure 1-13. The hoses and fluid lines have similar labels.

Unique service valves are used for each refrigerant to help prevent contamination. An R-12 system usually has Schrader-type service valves, while metric-thread, quick-connect fittings are used on an R-134a system.

Using Manifold Gauge Sets

A manifold gauge set consists of the center manifold and two or three gauges. The gauge set is used to:

- Monitor the pressure inside an operating system
- Monitor and control the flow of refrigerant into the system during charging
- Access the system for discharging

Valves at either end of the gauge manifold control which system pressure, high-side or low-side, is applied to the central manifold area. One hose connects the low-pressure gauge to the low-pressure side of the system, and a second hose connects the high-pressure gauge to the high-pressure side. A third hose connection in the middle of the manifold is used for adding or removing refrigerant. An evacuation pump, refrigerant supply cylinder, or refrigeration oil canister attaches to the center fitting.

With both valves closed, the gauges register the pressure in each side of the system. Opening the low-side valve connects the low-side of the system through the manifold to the center port, so refrigerant can be added or removed. Opening the high-side valve connects the high-side to the central area of the manifold, exposing high-side pressure to the central connection. Typically, a low-pressure gauge registers between about 30 in-Hg (760 mm-Hg) of vacuum to 120 psi (830 kPa) of pressure. The high-side gauge reads pressure only, generally in the 0 to 600 psi (0 to 4,100 kPa) range.

Connecting the Fittings

Service valve locations vary; the easiest way to find them is first to identify the high and low-sides of the system. Trace the refrigerant line that runs from the condenser to the compressor. This is the high-side of the system and the high-side service port will be somewhere in that line, often near the compressor outlet or on the receiver-drier. The refrigerant line that runs between the compressor

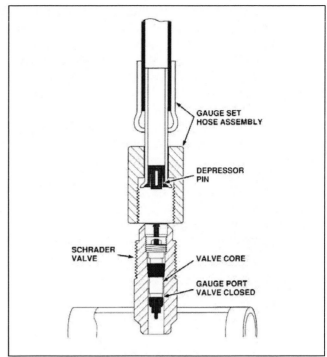

Fig. 1-14. *Schrader valve connections are used to service an R-12 system.*

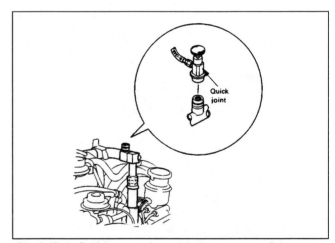

Fig. 1-15. *An R-134a system has quick-disconnect type fittings on the service ports.*

suction port and the evaporator is on the low-pressure side, and the service valve is generally located in this line or on the accumulator. To connect a manifold gauge set:

1. Connect the low-pressure gauge hose to the service valve located between the evaporator and the compressor suction port
2. Connect the high-side pressure gauge hose to the high-side fitting between the compressor and orifice tube or TXV
3. The middle hose connection is for system service. Some gauge sets have a tee or splitter valve connection, for connecting the refrigerant supply and evacuation pump with separate valves

Threaded Schrader valves are the most common type of service port in R-12 systems, figure 1-14. Larger, metric-thread, quick-connect service valves are used on R-134a systems, figure 1-15. In both types of systems, the high and low-side connectors are slightly different sizes to prevent attaching the gauges backwards. Follow these guidelines:

- Make sure the shutoff valves are within 12 inches (30 cm) of the service ends of the gauge hoses
- Close shutoff valves before removing them from the system service fittings
- Keep the gauge shutoff valves closed at all times when not in use
- After disconnecting the gauge hoses from a system, connect them to a recovery unit and remove any refrigerant from them

Manifold Gauge Procedures

Manifold gauges let you determine where and at what pressure to deliver refrigerant. The valve opens or closes a passageway to the center service port and hose. Some things to remember when using the valves:

- System testing—keep the valves closed so they read the pressures of each side of the system
- Discharging—connect the center port to a refrigerant recovery and recycling system and open both valves
- Leak-testing—with the engine off, connect the center service hose to a refrigerant supply, close the low-side valve, and open the high-side valve
- Vapor charging—connect a refrigerant supply to the center port, close the high-side valve, and open the low-side valve

Never vent R-12 or R-134a to the air; use a recovery system. When leak-testing, use a minimal amount of refrigerant of about one pound. After leak-testing, recover the refrigerant.

Evaluating Gauge Readings

The pressure read by the manifold gauges varies with refrigerant temperature. The low-side gauge monitors the pressure as the refrigerant enters the compressor, and the high-side gauge measures refrigerant pressure as it leaves the condenser or compressor. If the temperatures of either side are abnormally high or low, the pressure readings will also be abnormal.

Check specifications for normal pressures at various temperatures. Typical high-side readings for an R-12 system at an ambient temperature of about 90°F (32°C) are 180 to 205 psi (1240 to 1415 kPa). High-side pressure is slightly higher for an R-134a system, and typically ranges from about 215 to 240 psi (1470 to 1665 kPa) at the same temperature. On humid days, the high-side pressure will be at the high end of the range.

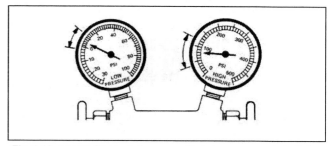

Fig. 1-16. *A low refrigerant charge results in low pressure in both the high and low-side.*

Gauge Readings and System Condition

When the gauges do not read the specified pressures, there is a system malfunction. Some abnormal readings and possible causes are described next.

Low-side low and high-side low, figure 1-16

Condition 1

Low Side:	Low
High Side:	Low
Sight Glass:	Constant stream of bubbles
Evaporator Discharge Air:	Only slightly cool
Diagnosis:	Low refrigerant charge, possible leaks
Remedy:	Locate leaks. Discharge system and repair leaks. Recharge.

Condition 2

Low Side:	Very low
High Side:	Very low
Sight Glass:	No bubbles, no liquid evident or faint fog
Evaporator Discharge Air:	Warm
Diagnosis:	Refrigerant charge excessively low, possible serious leaks
Remedy:	Add partial refrigerant charge. Locate leaks. Discharge system and repair leaks. Recharge.

Condition 3

Low Side:	Very low pressure,

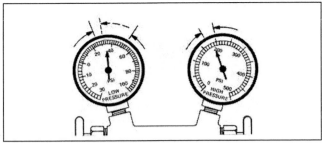

Fig. 1-17. A defective thermostatic switch causes a high low-side pressure with a normal high-side pressure.

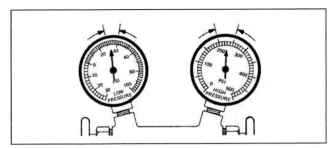

Fig. 1-18. Low-side high and high-side high pressures can be caused by a condenser malfunction, an overcharge, or contaminated refrigerant.

	or a vacuum
High Side:	Low
Evaporator Discharge Air:	Only slightly cool
Expansion Valve:	Inlet is cool, possibly frosted, or sweating heavily
Diagnosis:	Restricted TXV or orifice tube
Remedy:	Remove and inspect expansion valve inlet screen. If dirty, replace screen and receiver-drier. An orifice tube clogged with material can indicate a failing compressor.

Condition 4

Low Side:	Very low
High Side:	Low; may read normal to high if restriction is immediately downstream of the service valve
Evaporator Discharge Air:	Only slightly cool
Liquid Line:	Cool, possibly frosted, or sweating heavily
Receiver-Drier:	Possibly frosted or sweating heavily
Diagnosis:	Restriction in receiver-drier or liquid line
Remedy:	Discharge system, replace receiver-drier, liquid line, or other defective parts. Recharge.

Low-side cycles high and high-side normal, figure 1-17

Condition 5

Low Side:	Compressor cycles off higher than normal; compressor cycles close to normal; reduced cycle range
High Side:	Normal
Compressor:	Cuts in and out too rapidly
Diagnosis:	Defective thermostatic or pressure cycling switch
Remedy:	Replace thermostatic switch.

Condition 6

Low Side:	Compressor cycles off higher than normal; compressor cycles higher than normal
High Side:	Normal
Evaporator Discharge Air:	Warms excessively when compressor is off
Diagnosis:	Misadjusted thermostatic switch or defective pressure-cycling switch
Remedy:	Adjust or replace switch.

Low-side high and high-side high, figure 1-18

Condition 7

Low Side:	High

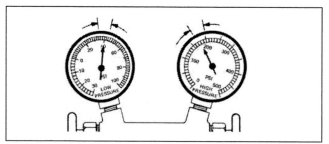

Fig. 1-19. *Insufficient high-side restriction or too short compressor "on-time" causes low-side pressure to rise while high-side pressure rerestrictionmains normal.*

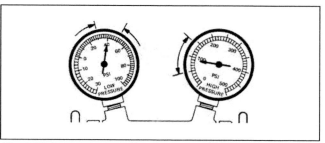

Fig. 1-20. *A compressor malfunction causes high low-side pressure and low high-side pressure.*

High Side:	High
Sight Glass:	Possible occasional bubbles
Evaporator Discharge Air:	Warm
Liquid Line:	Very hot
Diagnosis:	Condenser malfunction, overcharge, or refrigerant contamination
Remedy:	Check condenser for obstructions and reduced airflow. Check engine cooling system performance, including clutch-type fan. Discharge, repair, and recharge system.

Condition 8

Low Side:	High
High Side:	High
Sight Glass:	Occasional bubbles
Evaporator Discharge Air:	Warm to slightly cool
Diagnosis:	Large amount of air in system
Remedy:	Discharge system and replace receiver-drier or accumulator. Recharge.

Condition 9

Low Side:	High
High Side:	Normal to high
Evaporator Discharge Air:	Warm
Evaporator:	Heavy sweating

Suction Line:	Heavy sweating
Diagnosis:	Expansion valve stuck open or temperature-sensing bulb inoperative
Remedy:	Clean contact surfaces of sensing bulb and evaporator outlet pipe. Reinstall sensing bulb, making sure its metal band firmly secures it. If manifold pressures are still high, evacuate system, replace expansion valve and receiver-drier, and recharge. Recheck system for performance and leakage.

Low-side high and high-side normal, figure 1-19

Condition 10

Low Side:	High
High Side:	Normal
Evaporator Discharge Air:	Warm or only slightly cool
Diagnosis:	Insufficient high-side restriction or too short compressor "on-time"
Remedy:	Replace defective clutch cycling switch or missing O-ring at orifice tube.

Low-side high and high-side low, figure 1-20

Condition 11

Low Side:	High
High Side:	Low

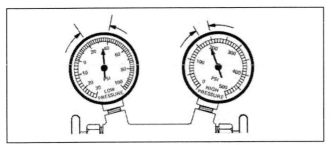

Fig. 1-21. *Air or moisture can cause poor cooling, even with normal system pressures.*

Sight Glass:	Clear
Evaporator Discharge Air:	Warm to slightly cool
Diagnosis:	Malfunctioning compressor
Remedy:	Verify proper control valve operation on a variable-displacement compressor system. Discharge system and replace the compressor and receiver-drier or accumulator. Recharge.

Condition 12

Low Side:	Low
High Side:	Normal to low
Evaporator Outlet:	Cold or frosted
Diagnosis:	Restricted high-side
Remedy:	Replace restricted expansion device.

Low-side normal, high-side normal, poor cooling, figure 1-21

Condition 13

Low Side:	Normal but constant; does not indicate cycling or modulation
High Side:	Normal; may be slightly high or low
Sight Glass:	Possible occasional bubbles
Evaporator Discharge Air:	Only slightly cool
Diagnosis:	Some air or moisture in the system
Remedy:	Verify the control system is not adding heat to the air. Test

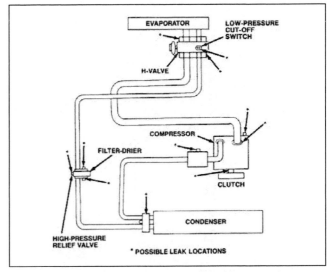

Fig. 1-22. *Fittings and connections are common sources of refrigerant leaks; check the entire system for leakage when servicing the air conditioner.*

for leaks, discharge, and repair as necessary. Replace receiver-drier or accumulator. Check compressor oil level. Recharge.

Condition 14

Low Side:	Normal; may drop into vacuum due to water freezing in the system
High Side:	Normal; will drop if low-side drops
Sight Glass:	Possible tiny bubbles
Evaporator Discharge Air:	Cold but becomes warm when low-side pressure drops into vacuum
Diagnosis:	Excessive moisture in system
Remedy:	Replace receiver-drier or accumulator. Evacuate and recharge.

LEAK DETECTION TESTING

Leaking refrigerant is the main cause of A/C problems. Signs of leaks include:

- Low manifold gauge readings
- Oily deposits on fittings or hoses
- Foam, bubbles, or oil streaks at the sight glass

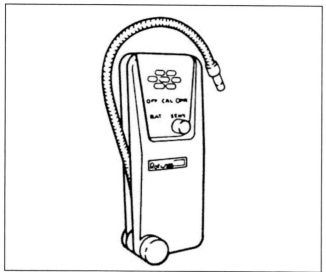

Fig. 1-23. *A typical electronic leak detector sounds an alarm and lights a warning lamp when refrigerant is picked up by the sensing probe.*

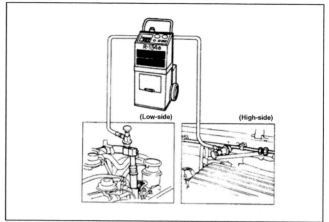

Fig. 1-24. *Using a recovery and recycling station to discharge the system.*

Always perform a leak test during routine service. Refrigerant leaks are often found where parts join together, especially if they are made of different materials. Parts that move in relation to each other, such as hoses that flex with engine torque, are also vulnerable. Refrigerant is heavier than air, so concentrations of leaking refrigerant are often found underneath components. Always check the entire system in case there is more than one leak, figure 1-22. Common leakage points include:

- Compressor seals
- Refrigerant line connections
- Pinholes in the accumulator, receiver-drier, evaporator, or condenser

A large leak is fairly easy to locate—look for oil on hoses, connections, or seals. If the system has been leaking for quite a while, the oily residue will collect dirt and appear greasy. However, not all leaks are easy to find. Besides a visual inspection, there are several ways to detect leaks:

- Leak detection with fluorescent dye
- Electronic leak detector

Dye Leak Detection

Dye leak detection involves charging the system with fluorescent dye. The dye does not cling to the refrigerant, but it mixes with the system lubricant. To check for leaks, add the dye, then run the air conditioner on high for about 15 minutes. Examine the system for dye leaking out of joints and connectors. An ultraviolet black light is used to find the dye that has leaked from the system. The dye remains in the system until the lubricating oil is changed. If no dye shows up, examine the

system again after 24 hours. Once the leak is located, perform the needed repairs. Check the service manual before adding dye; doing so may void the warranty on some systems.

Electronic Leak Detection

Electronic leak detectors are the safest tool for tracking refrigerant leaks. A sensor at the end of a probe reacts to the refrigerant and triggers a light and tone, figure 1-23. Since R-12 and R-134a have different chemical compositions, a separate electronic leak detector is needed for each type of refrigerant. However, dual units that can be switched to sense one refrigerant or the other are available. Electronic detectors are sensitive, so a high concentration of refrigerant in the air may trigger them. To find exactly where the leak is, work in a well-ventilated area moving the probe around all suspect components and connections.

REFRIGERANT AND REFRIGERATION OIL

R-12 and R-134a are incompatible, as are the refrigeration oils used in the two systems. An R-12 system uses mineral oil, while an R-134a system uses a synthetic Polyalkylene Glycol (PAG) or ester oil. Using the wrong type of oil causes compressor failure.

Systems retrofitted for R-134a use usually have an ester oil, while factory installed R-134a systems use one of several PAG oil blends. Ester, mineral, and PAG oils are not compatible, so it is important to identify and top off a system with the correct oil.

Identifying Specified Refrigerant

R-12 is usually sold in white containers, while R-134a comes in a blue container. Recycled R-12 is also in white containers, marked with a Department of Transportation (DOT) code. Only properly trained and certified technicians may perform service procedures involving refrigerant charging, discharging, recovering, and recycling.

Recovering Refrigerant

In past years, technicians vented R-12 into the air when discharging A/C systems. Doing so is now illegal. You may not vent either R-12 or R-134a into the atmosphere. Select the correct recovery and recycling station, for either R-12 or R-134a, to collect refrigerant, figure 1-24. Each type of refrigerant requires a separate recovery and recycling system.

Due to the incompatibility of refrigerants and lubricants, it is important to determine what the system being serviced is charged with before beginning repairs. Be aware: Mixing refrigerants and oils not only damages the vehicle system, but also contaminates the recycling station, manifold gauge set, and other equipment used to service the system. Electronic refrigerant identifiers are available to reduce the chance of contamination. These units draw a small sample of refrigerant from the vehicle service ports, then analyze the chemical composition of the sample. Typically, an identifier works well for R-12 and R-134a, but will not recognize the aftermarket refrigerant blends.

Refrigeration Oil

Because the lubricating oil circulates with the refrigerant in an A/C system, discharging refrigerant into a recovery station removes oil from the system as well. Recycling equipment separates the oil from the refrigerant. When recharging the system, add the same amount of fresh oil as was removed. The system also loses refrigeration oil during component replacement. Most shop manuals specify how much oil to add after replacing each part. Remember to add mineral oil to an R-12 system and the correct synthetic to an R-134a system, and not to confuse the two. Follow the recommendation of the compressor manufacturer when selecting refrigerant oil.

Refrigerant oil is highly refined and dried to remove almost all water. The purity and dryness of the oil are crucial for proper system operation. When working with refrigerant oil:

- Keep oil containers sealed until use, as they attract moisture
- Store PAG oil in metal, not plastic, containers
- Keep fittings and surrounding areas clean
- Do not return used oil to the system; replace oil with the correct amount of fresh, clean oil
- Use the specified oil

The following steps help maintain the correct amount of oil in the system:

- Measure the amount of oil lost during system discharge, and add that much fresh oil
- Drain and measure the oil from replaced components, and add that amount of fresh oil
- Add the recommended amount of oil that does not drain from the inside of replaced components

SYSTEM SERVICE

An A/C system must be discharged before any fittings are opened for repairs. Once repairs are made, the system must be evacuated and charged to return it to working order.

Discharging and Evacuating the System

Discharge the system before removing or replacing any part. Recover the refrigerant, whether R-12 or R-134a, into a recovery tank and later recycle it. To minimize the amount of refrigerant escaping into the air:

- Use recovery equipment that has shutoff valves within 12 inches (30 cm) of the hose service ends
- Always follow the equipment instructions for using the recovery and recycling station

The following is a general refrigerant discharge and recovery procedure:

1. With the equipment shutoff valves closed, attach the hoses to the system service fittings.
2. Following equipment instructions, recover the refrigerant until the system shows vacuum.
3. Turn off the equipment for five minutes or longer.
4. Check system pressure:
   - If the system has pressure, repeat the recovery process
   - If the system holds a steady vacuum for two minutes, proceed
5. Close the equipment shutoff valves and disconnect them from the system service fittings.

Checking Compressor Oil Level

Inadequate lubrication is the most common cause of compressor failure. Contemporary compressors do not have oil reservoirs, they are lubricated by the refrigerant oil circulating in the system. A system that relies on the oil in the refrigerant as the sole source of lubrication generally contains about 5.5 to 6.5 ounces (160 to 190 ml) of oil. Older compressors with an oil reserve generally contain about 10 to 11 ounces (300 to 325 ml) of oil. Oil is lost from the system when:

- A part is replaced, but the amount of oil it contained is not replaced
- The system is discharged too rapidly
- System pressure is lost through a leak

Traditionally, replacement compressors for an R-12 system are filled with enough oil to charge the system. However, newer compressors are shipped dry so they can be used with either R-12 or R-134a and must be filled with the correct amount of the proper oil for the system being serviced.

Minimize oil loss by discharging the system only when necessary and keeping the discharge rate slow.

Cleaning the System

A/C refrigerant system flushing is normally recommended whenever a compressor fails or a desiccant bag ruptures. Refer to the OEM service manual for additional information when possible. If information is not available, use the following procedure to flush the A/C system:

1. Discharge the A/C system as previously described.
2. Disconnect all A/C refrigerant line fittings and discard O-rings.
3. Remove orifice tube or TXV and discard.
4. Use an approved flushing vessel and flushing liquid. Starting with the evaporator core, slowly force the liquid in the bottom of the core until liquid flows from the top of the core. Continue until only clean, clear liquid flows out of the top. Stop the flow and allow five minutes before draining.
5. Repeat step four to properly flush the condenser.
6. Place caps on one end of the A/C lines. Fill the lines with the flushing liquid and allow five minutes before draining the liquid.
7. Blow the lines, evaporator and condenser out with pressure regulated dry nitrogen. (Shop air contains moisture and contaminants, which would recontaminate the A/C system.)
8. Replace the accumulator or receiver-drier.
9. Install a new orifice tube or TXV.
10. If required, replace the compressor with a new or rebuilt unit. (Follow OEM specs for correct quantity of oil to be added.)
11. Before reconnecting the refrigerant lines, add the correct amount of oil to the accumulator, evaporator, and condenser required by the OEM's specifications. Tighten all lines and fasteners to OEM specifications.
12. Evacuate and recharge the A/C system as described in Chapter One.

Charging the System

Before charging a system, consult the factory shop manual for the vehicle you are working on. Determine what type of system it is, its capacity, and if the compressor oil must be filled before charging. There are

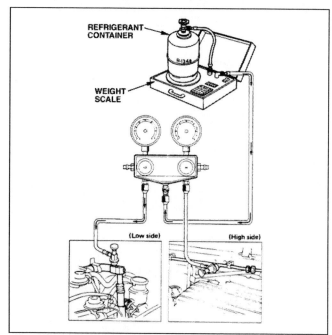

Fig. 1-25. *Using a scale to charge a system by weight.*

two charging methods:

- Liquid charging—add liquid refrigerant through the high-side service valve with the compressor off; liquid charge only with the engine off
- Vapor charging—add gaseous refrigerant through the low-side service valve while the compressor is running

Know the system capacity to avoid overfilling it, as little as a quarter-pound overcharge can damage orifice tube systems. Factory systems state the capacity on a sticker located either on or near the compressor, or on the radiator support. An accurate way to monitor how much refrigerant is being added is to place the refrigerant tank on a scale and watch the weight decrease as the refrigerant is drawn into the system, figure 1-25.

Liquid Charging

A small amount of refrigerant can be liquid charged into the high-side of the system after evacuation. To completely liquid charge the system through the high-side, a pump is needed to force the refrigerant in. If the low-side service port is on an accumulator, the system can be liquid charged on the low-side while running the engine. On systems without an accumulator, first liquid charge the high-side, then switch over to the low-side and complete by starting the engine and vapor charging.

Liquid charging is quicker than vapor charging, but the compressor must not be running when the high-side service valve is open, as this can rupture the refrigerant container. Follow this procedure:

1. Attach manifold gauges to the system. Connect

the service hose to a recovery station and discharge the system. Close both service valves to maintain the vacuum and disconnect the recovery station.

2. After connecting a vacuum pump to the manifold service hose, evacuate the system for at least 30 minutes. Close both valves when finished.

3. Connect the service hose to a refrigerant supply. Open the valve on the refrigerant supply to pressurize the service hose.

4. Open the high-side valve to direct the refrigerant supply into the high-side. The refrigerant container must be turned upside down or the valves on a bulk dispenser or charging station must be set correctly so that liquid refrigerant enters the system.

5. Close the high-side valve before changing refrigerant containers. Connect the new container to the service hose and open the high-side valve.

6. Complete system charging with the specified amount of refrigerant, adding new containers as necessary. Do not overcharge.

7. Turn the refrigerant supply valve off, close the manifold valve, and run the engine for about a minute to stabilize the system.

8. Check system performance.

9. Remove the manifold gauges, and replace all protective caps.

Vapor Charging

Vapor charging is the process of adding refrigerant through the low-side service valve while the compressor is running. Vapor charging can be performed from pound cans, drums, bulk cylinders, and charging stations. Vapor charge a system as follows:

1. Attach manifold gauges to the system. Connect the service hose to a recovery station and discharge the system. Close both service valves to maintain the vacuum and disconnect the recovery station.

2. After connecting a vacuum pump to the manifold service hose, evacuate the system for at least 30 minutes. Close both valves when finished.

3. Connect the service hose to a refrigerant supply. Open the refrigerant supply valve to pressurize the service hose.

4. Open the high-side valve with the engine off. Observe the low-side gauge to be sure the system is not restricted. Close the valve.

5. Open the low-side valve to direct the refrigerant supply through the low-side service valve. When charging from a bulk source, be sure to position the valves so that only vapor is added. When charging from a canister, it must be upright so liquid does not enter the system.

6. Start and run the engine at about 1,200-1,500 rpm with the A/C control lever OFF.

7. Engage the compressor by setting the control lever to NORM and the blower speed on HIGH. This draws in refrigerant faster. Be sure to add only vapor when the system is running.

8. Add the specified amount of refrigerant. Do not overcharge.

9. Turn the refrigerant supply valve off, close the manifold valves, and run the engine for about a minute to stabilize the system.

10. Check system performance.

11. Remove the manifold gauges and replace all protective caps.

1. A clicking noise at the compressor is likely to signal:
   a. Loose compressor mounts
   b. A defective compressor clutch bearing
   c. Liquid refrigerant entering the compressor
   d. Internal damage to the compressor

2. The most likely cause of a thin stream of bubbles visible in the sight glass of an R-12 system with the engine running at idle would be:
   a. Too much refrigerant
   b. Low refrigerant level
   c. Normal operation
   d. Too much oil in the system

3. Frost on the evaporator suction hose indicates a defective:
   a. Expansion valve
   b. Evaporator
   c. Receiver-drier
   d. Compressor

4. Which type of A/C system has an accumulator in the evaporator-to-compressor line but no receiver-drier in the evaporator inlet line?
   a. Externally equalized combination-valve
   b. Valves In Receiver (VIR)
   c. Pilot Operated Absolute (POA)
   d. Cycling Clutch Orifice Tube (CCOT)

5. When running the A/C system to check performance, do all of the following, EXCEPT:
   a. Put the blower on HIGH
   b. Block all but one vent
   c. Close the car doors and windows
   d. Let the engine idle for 10 minutes

6. The service valves on an R-134a system are:
   a. Twist-on valves
   b. Schrader valves
   c. Stem valves
   d. Quick-connect valves

7. When using manifold gauges to test an A/C system:
   a. Open both valves
   b. Open only the high-side valve
   c. Open only the low-side valve
   d. Keep both valves closed

8. The most likely cause of low pressure on both the high and low-sides, and frost on the expansion valve inlet of an A/C system would be:
   a. Expansion valve may be starved of refrigerant
   b. Expansion valve stuck closed
   c. Expansion valve stuck open
   d. Condenser malfunction or overcharge

9. The best way to leak check an R-134a system is with a(n):
   a. Leak-detecting dye
   b. Halide torch
   c. Electronic detector
   d. Chlorine torch

10. Leak-checking with dye may:
    a. Void the system warranty
    b. Cause compressor failure
    c. Cause desiccant deterioration
    d. Clog the expansion valve

11. When discharging refrigerant from an A/C system:
    a. Capture escaping refrigeration oil for reuse
    b. Discharge the refrigerant into an empty can
    c. Open only the high-side service valve
    d. Continue until the system shows vacuum

12. The type of oil used in an R-134a system is:
    a. Polyalkylene glycol oil
    b. Mineral oil
    c. Hypoid compressor oil
    d. Type F synthetic oil

13. To minimize refrigerant release into the atmosphere, the length of the hose between the service equipment shutoff valves and the service connections should be less than:
    a. 6 inches (15 cm)
    b. 12 inches (30 cm)
    c. 18 inches (45 cm)
    d. 24 inches (60 cm)

14. The most common cause of compressor failure is:
    a. Liquid refrigerant entering the compressor
    b. Too much refrigerant in the system
    c. Not enough refrigerant in the system
    d. Not enough lubricant circulating through the compressor

15. During liquid charging, the:
    a. Compressor should be running
    b. High-side service valve should be open
    c. Low-side service valve should be open
    d. Engine cooling fan should be running

Chapter Two

REFRIGERATION SYSTEM COMPONENT DIAGNOSIS AND REPAIR

The refrigeration system includes the compressor and clutch, evaporator, condenser, lines and hoses, valves and other related parts. Since all of these components contain pressurized refrigerant, the system must be discharged and recovered before repairs that involve loosening fittings are made.

COMPRESSOR AND CLUTCH

The compressor and clutch work together to develop and maintain optimum system pressures. When either unit fails, the system cannot operate. The clutch, which drives the compressor, is belt-driven by the engine crankshaft. A worn or incorrectly adjusted drive belt or a slipping clutch reduces compressor efficiency and system performance suffers.

Drive Belt Service

Some engine systems use a single, long serpentine belt to drive accessories while others use several drive belts. With either type, check for:

- Glazing, deterioration, cracking, or fraying—replace as needed, figure 2-1
- Age—replace belts at 48,000 miles (76,000 km), or 4 years, or the recommended interval
- Improper tension—check with a tension gauge, figure 2-2

To replace a V-type drive belt:

1. Loosen the belt-drive unit and rotate it to relieve belt tension.
2. Slip the belt off of the pulleys.
3. Install the new belt, making sure the V-shape of the belt rests in the pulley groove.
4. Rotate the drive unit to tighten belt tension.
5. Tighten fasteners to specified torque.

To replace a serpentine drive belt:

1. Attach a breaker bar or suitable tool to the adjustment socket on the tensioner, figure 2-3.
2. Swing the breaker bar to move the tensioner pulley and relieve belt tension, and hold it in that position.
3. Slip the belt from the pulleys and release the tensioner.

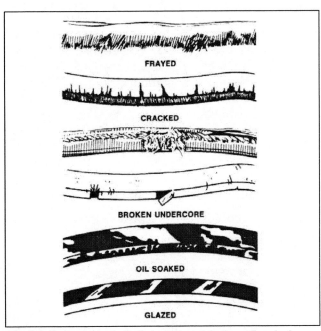

Fig. 2-1. *Replace drive belts that are glazed, broken, oil soaked, cracked, or frayed.*

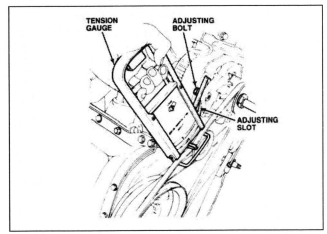

Fig. 2-2. *Use a tension gauge to make sure drive belts are correctly adjusted.*

4. Fit the new belt by routing it around all the accessories, then lever the tensioner down and slip the belt on to the tensioner pulley.
5. Once the belt is in place, remove the lever so the tensioner pulley applies the correct tension.

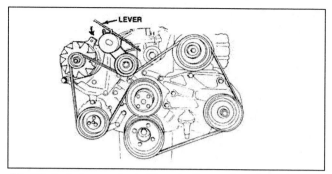

Fig. 2-3. *Typical serpentine belt layout with an automatic tensioner.*

Check specifications for the correct replacement belt. A correctly installed V-belt should ride on the sides of the pulley, not the bottom. The top of the belt should be flush with or not more than about 0.06 inch (1.5 mm) above the top of the pulley grooves, figure 2-4. With dual drive belts, replace both belts as a set—if one is bad, the other probably is too, and tension is unequal on mismatched belts. When installing a serpentine belt, be sure its grooves contact all the pulleys correctly.

Compressor Clutch Diagnosis and Service

Common compressor clutch failures include:

- Open field windings
- Slippage due to low supply voltage
- A seized or warped hub assembly
- A damaged or bent pulley
- A defective bearing

Begin troubleshooting at the field windings. Check the power and ground wire connections leading from the field coil. If they are good, the problem may be open windings in the coil preventing clutch operation or shorted field windings drawing excess current and blowing fuses. A field coil receiving a low voltage supply does not engage the clutch properly, resulting in slippage. Check the power supply with a voltmeter.

The clutch seizes if damaged or warped, or if the clutch plate surface is contaminated. Check the pulley to see if it is bent or damaged. Damage to the clutch hub or pulley can cause slippage, failure to engage, or failure to disengage. The clutch bearing should not fail if the drive belt tension is correct and the bearing dust seal is intact. If the bearing wears due to incorrect belt tension or contamination, replace it and the belt.

Checking Compressor Clutch Operation

The compressor clutch engages to drive the compressor shaft only when there is current through the clutch field winding. If the compressor operates with no current applied to the windings, the clutch is faulty. Another problem that may cause a clutch malfunction is a leaking front compressor seal that allows refrigerant and oil

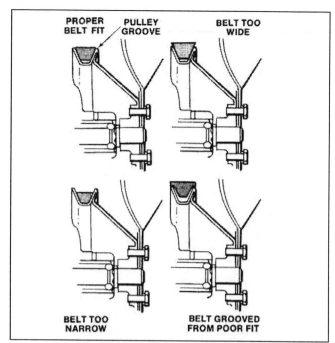

Fig. 2-4. *Check that V-belts are fully seated in the pulley grooves.*

to escape from the system. The oil can contaminate the clutch and cause slippage. To check clutch operation:

1. Switch the engine off and disconnect the compressor clutch power wire.
2. Use a jumper wire with an inline fuse to connect the clutch field winding to the positive battery terminal. The clutch should engage. If it does not:
   - Check the ground connection at the clutch
   - Check the clutch coil winding resistance; if open, replace the coil or clutch assembly
3. Make sure that when the clutch engages, the compressor shaft turns. If it does not, inspect the clutch.
4. With the A/C off, start the engine. If the clutch engages, remove the power wire to the clutch. If the compressor still turns, the clutch is seized and must be replaced.
5. Run the engine at 1,500 rpm with the A/C on MAX. Ensure that the clutch engages and the compressor turns.
6. With the clutch engaged, connect and disconnect the power lead to the clutch. The clutch should engage and disengage without excessive slippage. If it slips, check for:
   - Inadequate voltage or ground at the clutch field coil
   - Excessive air gap between the armature and pulley assembly
   - Excessive friction or binding limiting armature travel
   - Oily or worn clutch surfaces
   - A partially or fully seized compressor

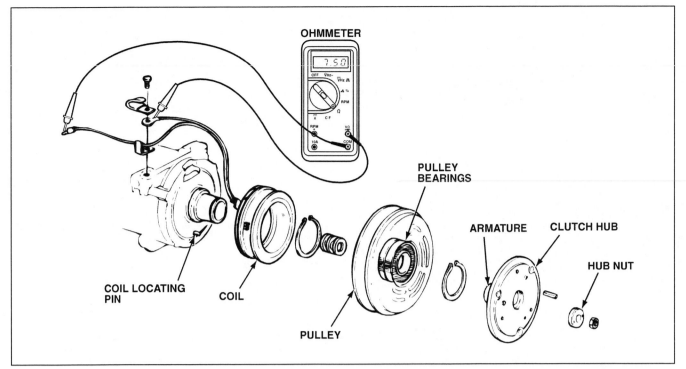

Fig. 2-5. Checking compressor clutch coil winding resistance with an ohmmeter.

7. Use an ohmmeter to measure coil resistance, figure 2-5. If it is not within specifications, reverse the ohmmeter leads and check again. If resistance is still not within specifications, replace the coil assembly.

Most late model automotive Heating, Ventilation, and Air Conditioning (HVAC) systems rely on the Powertrain Control Module (PCM) to engage or disengage compressor operations in response to the driver's request as well as other conditions. To control the clutch engagement, the PCM uses various inputs such as high or low pressure sensors in the A/C system and engine sensors like the Throttle Position (TP) Sensor, Engine Coolant Temperature (ECT) Sensor, etc.

For instance, when the A/C high-side pressure exceeds a predetermined point, the PCM opens the circuit to the compressor clutch relay. This action disengages the clutch and allows pressure to remain at a safe level. Conversely, when the A/C system pressure is very low indicating the possible loss of refrigerant, the PCM will not energize the relay control circuit preventing compressor operation. This action prevents compressor damage from the lack of circulating oil.

Follow the appropriate OEM procedures when diagnosing a PCM controlled compressor clutch. When replacing the PCM because of a compressor clutch failing to engage, the integrity of the compressor clutch diode must be checked. This diode protects the vehicle electronic systems from the voltage spike that occurs

when the clutch coil is de-energized. If the diode is defective, the new PCM may be damaged as well.

Servicing Compressor Clutches

Although the clutch mating surfaces eventually scar from normal operation, a badly scarred clutch can slip. If clutch wear is suspected, remove the clutch assembly and inspect the mating surfaces for cracks, heat checks, and scars that are deeper than 0.050 inch (1.3 mm). Replace the clutch if damage is found. Typical service procedures for the compressor clutch include:

* Clutch removal
* Bearing replacement
* Field coil replacement
* Clutch installation

Clutch Removal

Special tools, which are unique to the compressor being serviced, are generally required to remove the clutch for repairs or replacement. Failure to use the proper pulleys and seal removers can damage the compressor. To remove the clutch:

1. Remove the drive belt from the compressor pulley.
2. If there is enough room to work on the compressor clutch while it is on the vehicle, leave it in place. Otherwise, discharge the system, remove and cap the refrigerant lines, and remove the compressor from the vehicle.
3. Disconnect the clutch electrical wiring.
4. Remove the clutch plate and hub, which are held

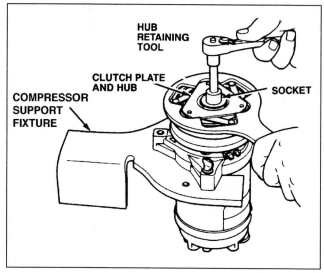

Fig. 2-6. Using a hub retaining tool to remove the clutch hub nut.

to the compressor shaft with a retaining nut or Torx-head screw. For most clutches, a special hub-retaining tool is used to prevent the clutch plate from rotating while removing the nut, figure 2-6. Never place the hub in a vise.

5. Some compressors have a snapring behind the clutch plate that retains the clutch assembly. If so, remove it, figure 2-7.
6. Use a special puller to separate the clutch assembly from the compressor shaft, figure 2-8.

When removing a clutch, do not apply pressure to the compressor shaft unless specifically recommended by the manufacturer. Generally, the puller seats on a shaft sleeve to prevent internal compressor damage. Do not attempt to pry the clutch off, as this can damage the assembly which is often made of aluminum.

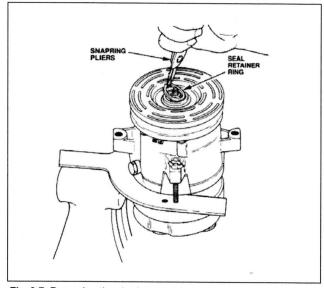

Fig. 2-7. Removing the clutch assembly snapring.

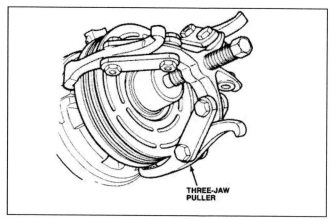

Fig. 2-8. Using a puller to remove the clutch assembly from the compressor.

Clutch Pulley Bearing Replacement

If the clutch pulley bearing is worn, replace it:

1. Remove the clutch assembly.
2. Most clutch bearings are press-fit in place and also have a snapring. Remove the snapring.
3. Support the clutch on a fixture and use a bearing driver and a soft-faced hammer to remove the old bearing from the housing, figure 2-9.
4. Inspect the old bearing to determine what caused it to fail, and correct any related compressor problems. For example, if the bearing is dirty, check seals for damage, and replace as needed.
5. Press or drive the replacement bearing into the housing using the appropriate tools to prevent damage during installation. Fully seat the bearing against the ridged stop.
6. Install the bearing snapring, if used.
7. Install the clutch assembly on the compressor and return the system to working order.

Field Coil Replacement

When there is a problem with the field coil, the clutch does not work properly. Field coils fail when the:

- Windings are open or shorted
- Connections from the wire harness to the field coil fail

Field coils have a nominal resistance of about 3 to 5 ohms, and carry a current between 2.5 and 3.5 amperes. When checking the field windings, keep the following in mind:

- Shorted windings produce higher current and lower resistance readings
- Open or resistive connections cause lower current and higher resistance readings

Field coils are encased in epoxy. If the problem is in the coil winding itself, replace the entire field coil. Resistive or intermittent connections can be repaired. To replace a field coil on a stationary-field clutch:

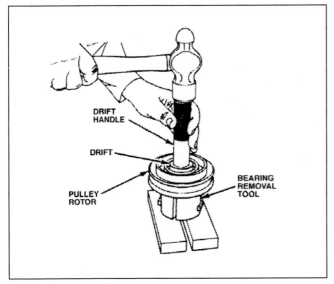

Fig. 2-9. Driving the bearing out of the clutch assembly.

1. Remove the compressor clutch assembly.
2. Remove the fasteners holding the field coil in place—some units attach to the compressor housing with screws; others are retained by a snapring.
3. Check field coil resistance, and inspect mounting surfaces and electrical connections. Repair connections as needed and replace the field coil if resistance remains out of specifications.
4. Install the replacement unit by attaching it at the mounting surface with the screws or snapring.
5. Install the clutch assembly. Verify that the armature-to-pulley air gap is within specifications, then connect the electrical circuits and route wiring away from moving parts.

Compressor Clutch Installation

To install the compressor clutch:

1. Reinstall the stationary field coil.
2. Align the clutch with the compressor shaft keyway. Make sure the clutch is squarely aligned with the front of the compressor.
3. Using the correct installation tools, press, or drive with a soft-faced hammer, the clutch assembly onto the shaft until it seats against the locating ridges. Do not use excessive force.
4. Reinstall the snapring, if used.
5. Reinstall the front locking nut or bolt and tighten to specified torque.
6. Check the air gap and compare to specifications.
7. Spin the pulley. It should rotate freely and evenly.
8. Reinstall the compressor onto the vehicle. Reconnect the electrical circuits and install the drive belt.
9. Evacuate and charge the system. Then check compressor clutch and system operation.

Compressor Service

Overhauling a compressor is time-consuming and requires an assortment of special tools, so most shops simply replace a failed unit with a new or rebuilt one.

Compressor Mechanical Failure

Damaged internal parts can also cause compressor failure. Damage to the pistons, cylinder walls, swashplates, and other parts may be caused by:

- Insufficient refrigerant or lubricant
- Incorrect oil
- Collision damage
- System contamination
- Debris in the cylinder
- Incorrect assembly or disassembly

Inadequate lubrication is the most common cause of compressor failure; lack of lubrication causes excessive friction and overheating, which results in seized parts. Replace a seized compressor.

Compressor Contamination

Damage to A/C system parts can contaminate the compressor. Also, improper evacuation and charging procedures leave moisture in the system, which forms corrosive acids. If the compressor is contaminated, drain the oil to clean it, or replace it.

Removing and Replacing Compressors

Correct removal and replacement procedures for the compressor minimizes system contamination and prevents damage to hoses, connectors, and other components. Although exact procedures vary by model, most can be removed using the following general guidelines:

1. Disconnect electrical wiring at the compressor.
2. Discharge the system using a recovery and recycling station. Recycle the refrigerant and measure the oil lost from the system.
3. Remove accessory drive belts as needed.
4. Separate the hose fittings from the compressor and immediately seal or cap all openings to prevent moisture and dirt from entering the system.
5. Remove the fasteners holding the compressor to its mounting brackets, and lift the compressor and clutch assembly from the vehicle as a unit.

Flushing may be recommended to assure there would not be any contaminants remaining in the A/C system from a failed compressor, plugged orifice tube, receiver-drier, or accumulator. At the time of doing an R-12 to R-134a retrofit some manufacturers suggest flushing the system at this time also.

When installing a replacement compressor, make sure the new unit contains the correct amount of the recommended oil, tighten all fasteners to specified torque, fit a new drive belt and adjust it to the correct tension. If contamination or moisture damage is found in the old compressor, install a new receiver-drier as well. Be aware, receiver-drier or accumulator replacement may be required for warranty by the compressor rebuilder. Then, evacuate and charge the system with the correct amount of the proper refrigerant and operate the system to check performance.

Compressor Testing

Troubleshooting the compressor involves diagnosing the entire A/C system. The following hints are specific to the compressor.

Diagnosing Cycling Clutch Compressors

For a **cycling clutch** compressor, diagnose the cycling pattern. A rapid pattern, when the compressor runs for only a short time then shuts off, indicates a quickly dropping low-side pressure causing the pressure cycling switch to shut the compressor off. Rapid cycling may be caused by:

- Very low refrigerant level
- Restricted fixed-orifice tube

The opposite condition, a slow cycling pattern where the compressor runs longer than normal, occurs when the compressor cannot pull the low-side system pressure down far enough. During a long cycling pattern, the pressure cycling switch stays closed and the compressor continues to run.

Irregular compressor cycling, a combination of cycles that are too long or too short, is often caused by a faulty pressure cycling switch. Irregular cycling results in poor cooling, and possible causes are:

- Pressure cycling switch closing pressure too high—the compressor stays off too long; if the switch sticks open, the compressor does not engage at all
- Closing pressure too high—the compressor switches on too quickly and the off cycle is too short, possibly causing evaporator freeze-up
- Opening pressure too low—the compressor shuts off too quickly, shortening the cooling cycle
- Opening pressure too high—the compressor stays on too long, possibly causing overcooling and evaporator freeze-up

Noise and Vibration

Grinding or banging noises from a running compressor indicate mechanical failure. To diagnose a compressor-related noise or vibration complaint:

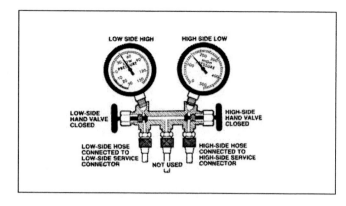

Fig. 2-10. *Internal compressor damage often results in high pressure on the low-side and low pressure on the high-side.*

1. Listen carefully while operating the system. Some system noise is normal. If in doubt, compare the noise and vibration levels to a similar system.
2. Check for missing or damaged compressor mounting bolts, bushings, and brackets. Tighten and replace as necessary.
3. Check for damaged or worn idler pulley, clutch, or clutch bearings. Check for damaged, loose, or misaligned drive belts. Replace or tension belts as necessary.
4. Check for debris that may be blocking the condenser and causing high system pressures. Check the engine cooling fan; an inoperative fan causes high system pressure.
5. With the engine running at idle, listen to and watch the clutch to make sure it is not hitting or rubbing against other parts.
6. If the noise comes from the front of the compressor, engage and disengage the clutch while the engine is idling to see if the noise stops or gets louder. If the noise gets louder or stops, check the clutch pulley bearing for wear or damage.
7. Perform a system pressure check. If the pressures are abnormally high or low, diagnose and replace components as needed.
8. Run the engine at 1,500 RPM. Listen for excessive rumble or knock that disappears when the clutch engages or disengages. Repair or replace the compressor as necessary.

To check a compressor for seizure:

1. Switch off the engine, and make sure the clutch is not engaged.
2. Remove the drive belt and try to turn the compressor shaft by hand.
3. If you hear grinding or feel resistance, the compressor is likely seized or the bearings are worn.

Cycling Clutch: A system that maintains refrigerant pressure by engaging and disengaging the electromagnetic compressor clutch.

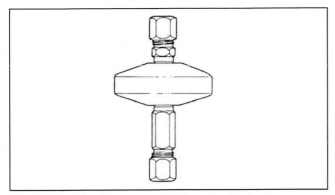

Fig. 2-11. An inline filter removes debris and contaminants.

Checking Compressor Operating Pressures

Characteristic manifold gauge readings from a fully charged but damaged compressor are high on the low-side and low on the high-side, figure 2-10. Typically, these conditions cause the compressor to be usually noisy with warm or only slightly cool discharge air from the evaporator. Poor compressor performance can be caused by:

- Defective reed valves
- Leaking compressor head gasket
- Worn or scored pistons, rings, or cylinders

EVAPORATOR, CONDENSER, AND RELATED PARTS

Along with the compressor, the evaporator and condenser are major A/C components. Hoses, fluid lines, the receiver-drier, and expansion and suction throttling devices handle and regulate the flow of refrigerant through the major components. Replacing any of these components requires evacuating the system.

Mufflers and Filters

Some systems use mufflers to control refrigerant flow noise, and a filter to purify the refrigerant may be used

as well. Inline filters are increasingly important for keeping systems clean. An inline filter can remove up to 90 grams of debris from a system and still allow adequate refrigerant flow, figure 2-11. Mufflers and filters cannot be repaired and are replaced if damaged or clogged.

Hoses and Fluid Lines

If hoses or fluid lines develop leaks, repair the connection or replace the hose, fluid line, or fitting.

Repairing Leaking Hoses

To repair a leak at a hose connection:

1. Slightly loosen then retighten the connection. Circulate air around the joint, then recheck it with a leak detector.
2. On O-ring connections, it may be necessary to discharge the system and replace the O-ring. Be sure to clean joint surfaces and lightly lubricate the new O-rings with fresh refrigeration oil. Tighten the connection, recharge the system, and check the joint with a leak detector.
3. If the line has replacement-type hose connections, tighten the hose clamp. Make sure that the clamp is correctly positioned.

If tightening the connection does not stop the leak, replace the hose with one of the same diameter, grade, length, and fittings as the old hose. Too-long or too-short hoses are prone to vibration damage. Also, a barrier-type hose is required for R-134a service and recommended for replacing any refrigerant hose.

Many late-model AC hoses have spring-lock fittings that require a special tool to remove them, figure 2-12. A damaged O-ring, loose or broken garter spring, debris, or corrosion can cause spring-lock fittings to leak. To repair:

1. Separate the coupling.

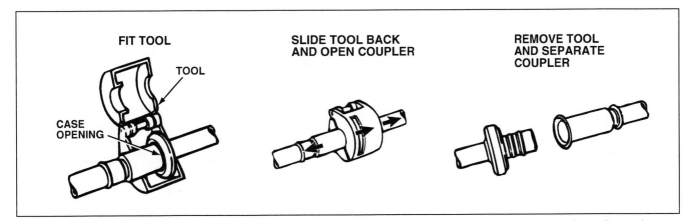

Fig. 2-12. Spring-lock couplings require a special tool that clamps around the fitting and is slid back to expand the garter spring so the coupler can be separated. Fit new O-ring before reconnecting.

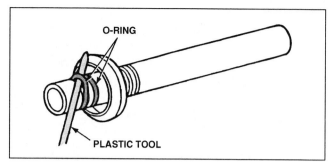

Fig. 2-13. Carefully remove O-rings with a plastic tool to avoid damaging the tubing.

2. Remove the old O-rings with a plastic tool to prevent damage to the tubing, figure 2-13.
3. If the garter spring is loose, broken, or damaged, use a small wire hook to pull it out of the cage. Install a new spring.
4. If needed, polish the inside of the female coupler with 600-grit emery cloth, then thoroughly clean it.
5. Lubricate new O-rings with the proper refrigeration oil, then install them.
6. Lubricate the inside of the female end, then join the coupler.

Replacing Refrigeration Lines

Replace rigid refrigeration lines in the case of collision damage, improperly tightened connections, or internal corrosion. Use new lines from the manufacturer for the best results.

Condenser and Evaporator

The condenser and evaporator are particularly susceptible to collision damage and plugging. Both can leak when cracks develop at seams and other stress points.

Condenser and Evaporator Inspection

Replace a condenser or evaporator if it has:

• Collision damage
• Leaks
• Unremovable clogging or debris
• Corrosion from moisture contamination

Symptoms of a defective condenser or evaporator include:

• Excessive high-side pressures, possibly with the pressure relief valve venting excess pressure and frost on the discharge line
• Severe compressor damage, suggesting that debris has contaminated the condenser
• Refrigerant loss, indicating possible leaks at the evaporator or condenser
• Areas of localized frost

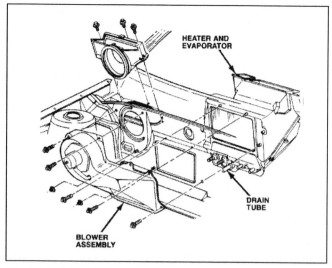

Fig. 2-14. The ventilation system plenum or module may need to be disassembled to remove the evaporator.

Condenser and Evaporator Service

In cases of extreme contamination, collision damage, or irreparable leaks, replace the condenser or evaporator. Use these guidelines:

• Do not remove the replacement part from its sealed bag until just before installation
• Do not remove the protective plugs from hose connectors prior to installing the hoses
• Make sure all connections are clean
• Lightly lubricate connectors with fresh refrigeration oil before installation
• Tighten connections to specifications

Evaporator Replacement

Procedures for removing and installing an evaporator vary by vehicle. The following general guidelines apply to any installation:

1. Discharge the system using a recovery and recycling station, recycle the refrigerant, and measure how much refrigeration oil was extracted.
2. If the evaporator and heater core are one unit, drain the cooling system.
3. Disconnect any electrical harnesses or thermostatic devices attached to the evaporator.
4. Disconnect, and immediately cap or seal, the refrigerant hoses from the evaporator.
5. Evaporator removal may require disassembling the ventilation system plenum or module, figure 2-14. Follow shop manual procedures.
6. Drain and measure any oil in the old evaporator.
7. Fit the new evaporator in place and connect the hoses using new O-rings. Coat hose connections with clean refrigeration oil to aid installation.

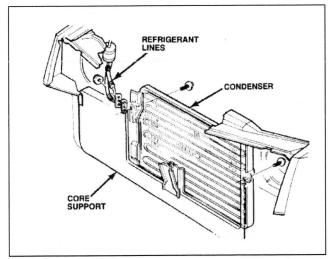

Fig. 2-15. The condenser generally attaches to the radiator core support with sheet-metal screws.

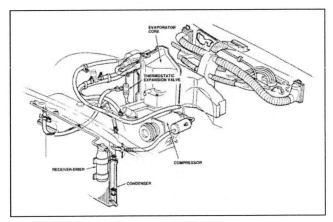

Fig. 2-16. The receiver-drier is on the high side of the system between the condenser and the expansion valve.

8. Add enough fresh refrigeration oil to replace the amount lost during discharge and evaporator removal, and also add the recommended amount of oil to compensate for what did not drain from the evaporator.

9. Evacuate and recharge the system, then check the system for leaks.

Condenser Replacement

To remove and install a condenser:

1. Discharge the system using a recovery and recycling station, recycle the refrigerant, and measure how much refrigeration oil was extracted.

2. Remove the fan shroud, radiator, grille, trim panels, or other items required to gain access to the condenser, figure 2-15.

3. Disconnect and seal or cap the refrigerant lines at the condenser.

4. Remove fasteners securing the condenser and lift it from the chassis. If the receiver-drier mounts on the condenser, remove both as a unit.

5. Drain and measure the oil in the condenser.

6. Fit the new condenser in place, install new O-rings, coat fitting connections with clean refrigeration oil, then connect the lines.

7. Install the radiator, fan shroud, and other parts removed for disassembly and fill the cooling system.

8. Add enough fresh refrigeration oil to replace the amount lost during discharge and evaporator removal, and also add the recommended amount of oil to compensate for what did not drain from the evaporator.

9. Evacuate and recharge the system, then check the system for leaks.

Evaporator Housing Service

Make sure the evaporator housing is clean so that condensation that forms on the coils can drain properly. Undrained water and debris grow bacteria that can release an unpleasant odor into the passenger compartment when the A/C is running.

Receiver-Drier Service

The receiver-drier is a high-pressure storage device located between the condenser outlet and expansion valve inlet, figure 2-16. A desiccant bag in the receiver-drier removes moisture from the system. The receiver-drier is replaced when there is:

- System or component contamination
- Refrigerant leaks
- Collision damage
- Excessive ambient air entering an open system
- Compressor replacement

The signs of receiver-drier problems include:

- Loss of refrigerant
- Moisture or debris contamination
- Desiccant particles in the system
- Refrigerant starvation due to receiver-drier blocked
- A significant temperature difference between the receiver-drier inlet and outlet
- Frost on the bottom of the receiver-drier

The receiver-drier is not serviceable and must be replaced when defective.

Receiver-Drier Replacement

To remove and replace the receiver-drier:

1. Discharge the system using a recovery and recycling station, recycle the refrigerant, and measure how much refrigeration oil was extracted.

2. Disconnect the receiver-drier inlet and outlet line

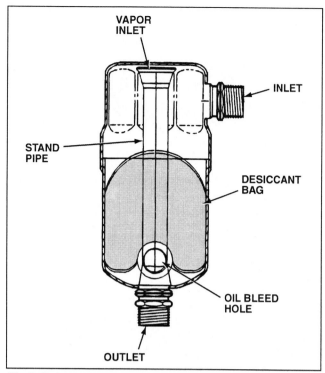

Fig. 2-17. An accumulator stores excess refrigerant and prevents liquid refrigerant from returning to the compressor.

unit as a liquid and must be vaporized before it can be picked up at the top of the accumulator and returned to the compressor. The accumulator also contains a desiccant to remove moisture from the system, figure 2-17.

A drain hole at the bottom of the accumulator standpipe allows oil and some refrigerant to return to the compressor. Because of the large desiccant bag and the considerable amount of oil retained by the accumulator, it is important to accurately measure and replace the lost oil when installing a new accumulator. Follow the service manual guidelines.

The accumulator is not serviceable and must be replaced when defective. Also, replace the accumulator whenever a refrigerant hose, compressor, condenser, evaporator, or other major component is replaced.

Accumulator Replacement

To remove and replace the accumulator:

1. Discharge the system, recycle the refrigerant, and measure oil extracted.
2. Disconnect the accumulator inlet and outlet line fittings and cap or seal them.
3. Remove the attaching hardware and lift the accumulator from the chassis.
4. Drain and measure any residual oil in the accumulator.
5. Install the replacement unit.
6. Add the correct amount fresh refrigeration oil.
7. Evacuate and recharge the system, then check the system for leaks.

Orifice Tube System Service

Fixed-orifice expansion tubes are found on late-model vehicles built by a number of manufacturers. Replace an orifice tube in the case of:

- Orifice clogging
- Inlet or outlet contamination or clogging
- Debris in the system

When an orifice tube fails, the symptoms are similar to those of a clogged expansion valve:

- Airflow through the evaporator warm or only slightly cool
- Very low low-side pressure and low to normal high-side pressure
- Sweating or frost on the line between the expansion tube and evaporator

Test for a defective orifice tube as follows:

1. Connect the manifold gauge set. Start and run the engine at 1,500 RPM for 10 minutes with the A/C on MAX, and the blower on HIGH.
2. Check the low-side gauge reading. If it is abnor-

fittings and cap or seal them. Also, disconnect any electrical wiring to the receiver-drier assembly.
3. Remove the attaching hardware and lift the receiver-drier from the chassis. On some systems, the condenser must be removed before the receiver-drier.
4. Drain and measure any residual oil from the old receiver-drier and transfer any switches or sensors from the old unit to the new one.
5. Install the replacement unit. Tighten the hose connection fittings to specifications before tightening the mounting bracket bolts.
6. Reconnect any electrical connections on the receiver-drier assembly.
7. Add enough fresh refrigeration oil to replace the amount lost during removal, along with the recommended amount of oil to compensate for what did not drain from the receiver-drier.
8. Evacuate and recharge the system, then check the system for leaks.

Accumulator Service

The accumulator is a device on the low-side of an orifice tube system that performs two functions: It serves as a storage container to hold excess refrigerant, and also prevents liquid refrigerant from returning to the compressor. The accumulator, which is located at the evaporator outlet, receives refrigerant in both liquid and vapor form. Refrigerant is stored at the bottom of the

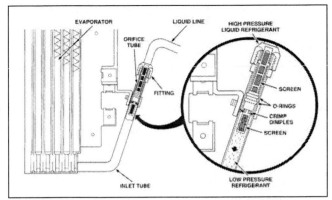

Fig. 2-18. The orrifice tube is located in the evaporator inlet line.

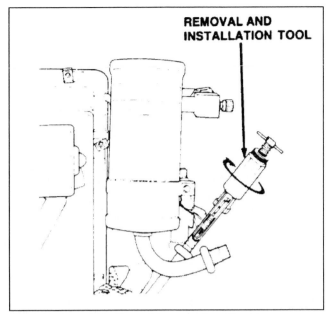

Fig. 2-19. A special tool is used to remove the orifice tube.

mally low and the high-side gauge indicates that pressurized refrigerant is available, suspect a problem with the orifice tube.

On most systems, the orifice tube is located in the evaporator inlet line, figure 2-18. O-rings on the outside of the tube hold it in place. The orifice tube, which is fragile, often breaks during removal. If this happens, use special extractor tools to remove the pieces. To replace the orifice tube:

1. Discharge the system using a recovery and recycling station, recycle the refrigerant, and measure how much refrigeration oil was extracted.
2. Disconnect the evaporator inlet line.
3. A special tool is used to remove the orifice tube, figure 2-19. Slide the inner sleeve of the tool over the tube until its notch slides over the end of the orifice tube, then engage the notch with a plastic tab on the tube. Rotate the outer sleeve counterclockwise to remove the orifice tube. Do not rotate the tool inner sleeve during removal. The inner sleeve is only to engage the orifice tube.
4. Coat the new orifice tube with clean refrigeration oil.
5. Push the new orifice tube into position until it bottoms against the stop.
6. Install a new top O-ring, and reconnect the evaporator inlet line.
7. Replace oil lost during discharge, then evacuate and charge the system.
8. Test the system for leaks.

On some designs, the orifice tube cannot be removed from the evaporator inlet line. If the orifice tube becomes clogged, install a new line with a built-in orifice tube.

Thermostatic Expansion Valve (TXV) Service

TXV and suction throttling devices regulate refrigerant pressure and flow at the evaporator inlet. A TXV failure can be caused by:

- Debris clogging the valve or inlet screen

- Moisture causing restrictions in the metering valve
- Moisture contamination and corrosion
- Damage to the capillary tube or bulb

The symptoms of a TXV failure depend on the nature of the problem. The most common cause of failure is a restricted TXV. Three major causes of TXV failure and some symptoms they produce are:

1. Valve stuck closed—the evaporator is starved of refrigerant, causing the following symptoms:
    - Airflow through the evaporator warm or only slightly cool
    - Low pressure on both the high and low-side
    - Sweating or frost on the TXV, which can result from a clogged TXV inlet screen
2. Valve stuck open, capillary and sensing bulb failure—the evaporator floods, causing the following symptoms:
    - Airflow through the evaporator warm or only slightly cool
    - Low-side pressure high
3. Intermittent TXV operation—the A/C works intermittently, causing the following symptoms:
    - Fluctuating output air temperature
    - Intermittent changes in low-side pressure readings
    - System operates normally when first started then stops cooling

Although it may appear to be a TXV problem, a loss of cooling after continued use is often caused by the receiver-drier allowing moisture into the system. In this case, ice forms in the TXV during system operation. When the system warms after shutting down, the ice melts, so the system works normally the next time it is

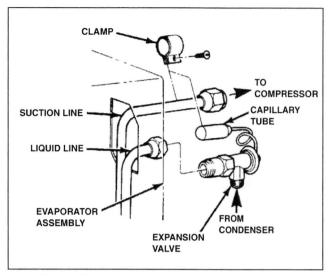

Fig. 2-20. *The TXV installs at the evaporator inlet*

switched on—until the ice re-forms.

Replacing the TXV

When installing or removing a TXV:

- Handle the capillary tube carefully, without bending or kinking it
- Insert the replacement tube fully into the mounting bracket or sleeve
- Make sure the replacement capillary bulb is installed in the same position as the original
- Replace any insulation you removed to gain access to the bulb

The TXV installs at the evaporator inlet, figure 2-20. Following is a typical TXV replacement procedure:

1. Discharge the system using a recovery and recycling station, recycle the refrigerant, and measure how much refrigeration oil was extracted.
2. Disconnect the TXV external equalization line, if used.
3. Remove any insulation that covers the capillary tube and bulb.
4. Remove the bracket holding the capillary bulb in position.
5. Disconnect, and immediately cap or seal, the refrigerant line fittings at the TXV, then remove it from the vehicle.
6. Inspect the TXV inlet screen for debris.
7. Fit the new TXV, install new O-rings if used, lubricate connections with fresh refrigeration oil, and tighten fittings to specification.
8. Replace the equalization line and capillary along with any insulation that was removed. Be sure to replace the capillary in its original position.
9. Replace oil lost during discharge, then evacuate and charge the system.
10. Test the system for leaks.

Service Valves

Service valves are generally welded to a rigid line, the receiver-drier, or the accumulator. The body of the valve is not serviceable. Leaking valve cores can be tightened or replaced. Replacement requires:

1. Discharge the system using a recovery and recycling station, recycle the refrigerant, and measure how much refrigeration oil was extracted.
2. Remove the valve core with a special tool.
3. Inspect the core seating area for burrs, stripped threads, and damage.
4. Install a new valve core.
5. Replace oil lost during discharge, then evacuate and charge the system.
6. Test the system for leaks.

High-Pressure Relief Device Service

A pressure relief valve is a spring-loaded mechanical safety device. If system pressure rises high enough to overcome the force of the relief valve spring, the valve lifts from its seat allowing refrigerant to escape. The valve remains open only long enough to reduce the system pressure below the setpoint. Pressure relief valves are mounted in the high side of the system. The location varies; look at the discharge port of the compressor, along the high-pressure line, and on the receiver-drier. A high-pressure cutout switch must be added when retrofitting an R-12 system with a pressure relief valve for use with R-134a.

Some systems have a high-pressure cutout switch mounted on the rear of the compressor to protect the compressor. This switch is wired in series with a low-pressure cutout switch and the ambient temperature sensor. When system pressure rises above a preset level, the high-pressure cutout switch opens to interrupt current to the compressor clutch.

When a pressure relief device triggers, diagnose the system to find what is causing the pressure buildup. When a relief valve cycles, both refrigerant and refrigeration oil escape from the system. Replace lost refrigerant and oil after repairing the cause of the high pressure.

1. Common compressor clutch failures include all of the following, ***EXCEPT***:
   a. Open field windings
   b. A seized or warped hub assembly
   c. Shorted pressure relief switch
   d. A damaged or bent pulley

2. A compressor clutch that remains engaged when the A/C is switched off is most likely caused by:
   a. Open field windings
   b. A seized clutch assembly
   c. Defective pressure sensing device
   d. Shorted field windings

3. Which of the following statements about a compressor front seal is ***NOT*** true?
   a. Some front seals can be serviced without removing the compressor from the vehicle.
   b. Some manufacturers recommend replacing the entire compressor if the front seal is leaking.
   c. Some front seals can be replaced without discharging the system.
   d. The clutch assembly must be removed from the compressor to access the seal.

4. The most likely cause of a compressor reed valve failure would be:
   a. Gaseous refrigerant entering the compressor
   b. Extremely low system pressure
   c. Insufficient refrigerant or lubricant
   d. Debris circulating in the system

5. The most likely cause of warm evaporator discharge air and manifold gauge readings that show high low-side pressure and low high-side pressure would be:
   a. Internal compressor damage
   b. Low refrigerant level
   c. Ice forming in the expansion valve
   d. An evaporator core restriction

6. After repairing a system that was contaminated by debris, it is advisable to:
   a. Flush the system
   b. Install an inline filter
   c. Overhaul the compressor
   d. Replace the expansion device

7. Which of the following symptoms is ***NOT*** an indication of a receiver-drier problem?
   a. High low-side pressure and low high-side pressure
   b. A significant temperature difference between the receiver-drier inlet and outlet ports
   c. Frost forming on the bottom of the receiver-drier assembly
   d. Poor system performance as a result of refrigerant starvation due to receiver-drier blockage

8. To find the receiver-drier, look:
   a. Between the condenser outlet and the expansion valve inlet
   b. Between the evaporator inlet and the condenser inlet
   c. Between the compressor inlet and the expansion valve inlet
   d. Between the expansion valve outlet inlet and the evaporator inlet

9. The most likely cause of excessive high-side pressure, the pressure relief valve venting, and frost on the evaporator discharge line would be a(n):
   a. Defective suction throttling device
   b. Contaminated receiver-drier
   c. Defective condenser
   d. Orifice tube failure

10. All of the following are signs of orifice-tube failure, ***EXCEPT***:
    a. Warm airflow from evaporator
    b. Frost on the orifice tube-to-evaporator line
    c. Low-side pressure low
    d. High-side pressure high

Chapter Three

HEATING AND ENGINE COOLING SYSTEMS DIAGNOSIS AND REPAIR

Heating problems include output air temperature that is too hot or too cold and incorrect air distribution through the ductwork. Passenger compartment heaters depend on the engine cooling system to provide a steady stream of coolant at normal engine operating temperature. Ensure the engine cooling system is functioning properly before performing any other heating system repairs.

HEATER/VENTILATION CONTROL SYSTEM DIAGNOSIS

An operational check, similar to the one described for A/C systems, is performed to diagnose the heating system.

System Operation Check

To check heating system operation, start and run the engine until it is at operating temperature; the upper radiator hose should feel warm. Select the HEAT mode, turn the temperature control to MAX, and the blower to HIGH. Check air temperature at the floor vents with a thermometer, and compare with a temperature chart.

System Diagnosis

Diagnose heater system window fogging, heat output, and ventilation problems to determine needed repairs.

Window Fogging

Fogging can result from ventilation system malfunctions or **heater core** problems. Although a sticky residue on the glass often indicates a heater core failure, the ventilation system must be checked as well.

Heating Problems

The heater can have one of three basic problems:

- No heat
- Not enough heat
- Too much heat

Possible causes of a no-heat condition include:

- Blocked coolant flow through the heater core—If the heater hoses are cool with the engine running, the problem may be a plugged heater core, hoses, hose fittings, or a faulty **heater control valve**
- Incorrectly positioned blend doors—If the heater hoses are warm but no heat is delivered to the passenger compartment, check for stuck blend doors, disconnected or broken control cables, or damaged ductwork
- Blocked air inlet ducts—If the airflow improves when the mode selector is changed to the RECIRC position, check for ductwork or cowl air intake blockage
- Defective blower or reduced current to blower—If the blower runs slowly or not at all, refer to blower service instructions

Possible causes of insufficient heat are:

- Faulty heater control valve—Ensure the valve opens and closes smoothly; check the valve controls for correct adjustment, defective control cables, a leak in the vacuum system, or a faulty electrical connection
- Kinked or clogged heater hose—Inspect hoses, especially at the end fittings, and replace as needed
- Contaminated cooling system or low coolant level—Check coolant level and condition, and check for rust or scale around the filler neck
- Blend doors out of position—Check for stuck blend doors, or disconnected or broken control cables
- Defective or incorrectly installed thermostat—Check thermostat type and operation
- Partially blocked heater core—Perform heater core tests

Heater Control Valve: A cable, vacuum, or electric valve on the heater core inlet that controls the rate of coolant flow into the heater core.

Heater Core: A heat exchanger through which hot coolant passes and releases its heat by conduction into a passing air stream.

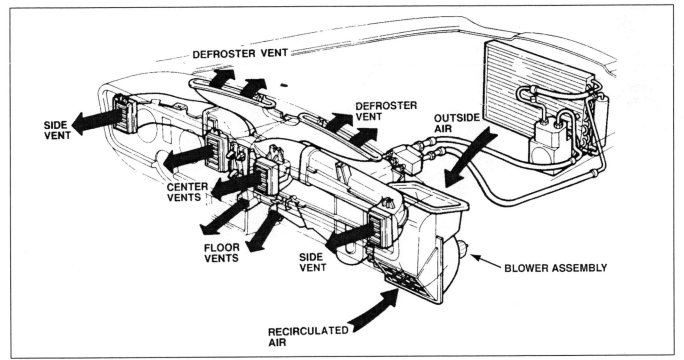

Fig. 3-1. *Typical HVAC ventilation system*

Possible causes of excessive heat are:

- Blend door stuck open—Ensure the linkage moves freely to the full open and closed positions
- Heater control valve stuck open—Check for misadjusted controller, broken valve, defective cable, vacuum system leak, or faulty electrical system

Most present day vehicles use a 195°F (91°C) thermostat. It is critical for the thermostat to function properly. The HVAC system, as well as emission and driveability conditions, depend on precise control of engine coolant temperatures for satisfactory operation.

Thermostats are designed to open and close at preset temperatures. If a thermostat does not operate properly it should be removed, inspected and tested. If the thermostat sticks open, the engine will warm up very slowly. If the thermostat sticks closed, the engine will overheat.

Use the following procedure to test the thermostat:

1. Drain the coolant until it is below the level of the thermostat, then remove the water outlet assembly.
2. Remove the thermostat. If visually faulty replace it, if not use the following test to determine correct operation.
   a. Place the thermostat and a thermometer in a container with 50/50 solution of water and ethylene glycol antifreeze. Place the container over a heater. While heating do not allow the thermostat or thermometer to rest on the bottom of the container; this will cause them to be at a higher temperature than the solution.
   b. Agitate the solution to ensure uniform temperature of the solution, thermostat, and thermometer.

The thermostat valve should start to open at 195°F (91°C). It should be fully opened after the temperature has increased 27°F (15°C). If the thermostat does not operate at the temperature specified, replace it; it cannot be adjusted.

Ventilation System Problems

Many ventilation system problems involve fogged windows and poor air circulation in the vehicle. The three basic ventilation problems are:

- No airflow
- Not enough airflow
- Misdirected airflow

When dealing with complains of no airflow, determine whether there is no airflow in the entire passenger compartment or only at a certain vent. If only one vent is working improperly, check the duct leading to that vent. Also check the condition of the vent door and cables.

Little or no airflow from all vents can be caused by HVAC system air intake or blower problems. To check, set the heater controls to VENT mode, switch on the blower, and operate the fan at each setting. If you can not hear the blower increase in speed, the problem is probably related to the blower motor, figure 3-1. Refer to the appropriate procedures.

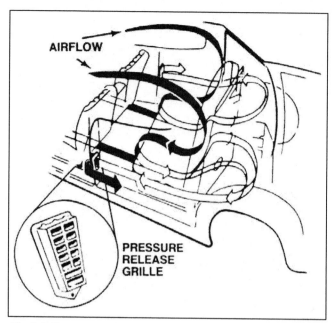

Fig. 3-2. Passenger compartment airflow depends on a clear outlet path for proper circulation.

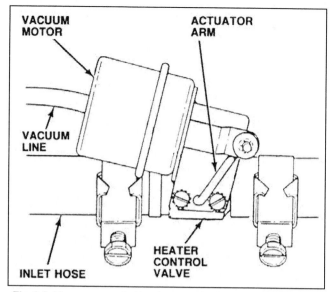

Fig. 3-3. Vacuum-operated heater control valve operation is checked with a hand-operated vacuum pump.

If you can hear the blower increase in speed, but there is little or no airflow, the problem is probably in the HVAC air intake system. Typical HVAC air intake problems are:

- Cowl intake blockage
- Intake air door stuck shut or not operating smoothly

If airflow is insufficient, check for:

- Blocked vent grills
- Partial blockage of the screen covering the cowl intake vent
- Partial or total blockage of the air ducts
- Incorrectly adjusted vent doors

Both inlet and outlet ducts must be clear, since air can enter the vehicle only if there is an outlet for the stale air to exhaust, figure 3-2. Make sure that the flaps in the vent grills open and close easily.

Heater Control Valve

Most heating systems use a heater control valve to regulate coolant flow into the heater core. The valve may be actuated by a cable, vacuum servomotor, or electric solenoid. To check the valve:

1. Determine whether the valve is normally open or normally closed.
2. Check valve position when it is not actuated, then switch the controls and monitor valve operation. A correctly operating valve opens and closes smoothly and completely.

A vacuum-operated heater control valve on a blend door system is usually open until a vacuum signal closes it, figure 3-3. Use a vacuum pump to check whether the valve opens smoothly and evenly with the correct amount of vacuum applied.

ENGINE COOLING SYSTEM SERVICE

The engine cooling system is the link between engine heat and the passenger compartment heating system. The engine cooling system must work well for the heating system to function properly. The engine water pump, which is belt-driven, provides the coolant circulation; service and adjust drive belts as previously described. Also, inspect cooling system hoses for:

- Hardness, cracks, brittleness
- Sponginess or interior damage
- Loose connections or leakage
- Age, figure 3-4

Hose replacement intervals of about 48,000 to 50,000 miles (76,000 to 80,000 km) as preventive maintenance may be recommended by the vehicle manufacturer. Check the cooling system for seepage and rust damage at the:

- Core plugs
- Water pump shaft seal
- Water pump and thermostat gaskets

Inspect the radiator for:

- Rust or oil in the coolant
- Leaks or corrosion at tank seams
- Kinked or damaged overflow tubes
- Clogged fins or air intake paths
- Loose or missing mounting bolts
- Incorrect coolant level in the overflow tank
- Leaves or other debris blocking the radiator
- Green corrosion on the outside of radiator tubes

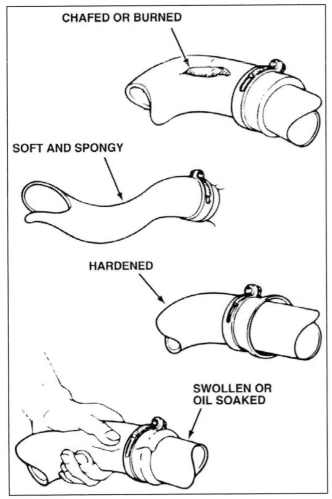

Fig. 3-4. Inspect all coolant hoses for damage.

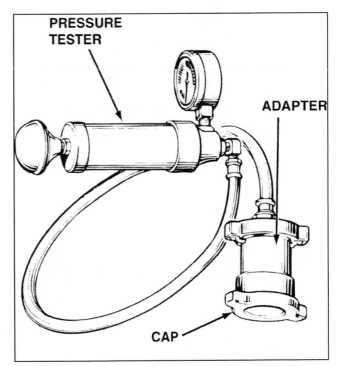

Fig. 3-5. Inspect and test the radiator pressure cap.

Check the heater enclosure and plenum for:
- Rust, indicating heater core leakage
- Loose hose connections
- Loose mounting bolts
- Air leaks and missing or detached ducts

An indication of an air leak is a fogged windshield, possibly with an oily film on the inside of the glass.

Check the water pump for:
- Leakage around the pump housing, shaft seal, hose connections, and gasket sealing surfaces
- Misalignment with the drive pulley
- Looseness, sideplay, or endplay in the water pump shaft bearing

If there is a fan clutch, check it for:
- Fluid leakage
- Noisy or rough operation when rotated by hand
- Excessive shaft looseness

If there is an electric fan, check it for:
- Loose electrical connections
- Damaged or poorly routed wiring
- Excessive endplay or sideplay in the motor shaft
- Operation

Check any type of fan for:
- Bent or cracked fan blades
- Binding on its shaft

The radiator fan shroud increases radiator and fan efficiency by forcing the fan airflow through the radiator core, so make sure it is present and securely fastened.

Inspect the radiator cap for:
- Looseness at the filler neck
- Brittle or damaged seal
- Sufficient spring action
- Correct pressure rating, figure 3-5

Test the radiator pressure cap using a cooling system pressure tester and an adapter as follows:

1. Attach the cap to one end of the adapter, then connect the opposite end to the tester.
2. Pump the tester until the cap vents and observe the gauge reading. The cap should vent when pressure exceeds the rating by one to three pounds. If not, replace the cap.
3. Allow the pressure to stabilize.
4. Observe the gauge; it should hold within one or two psi of the cap rating for one minute. If the gauge reading drops, the cap is bad; replace it.

A pressure cap vacuum valve that is not venting properly causes the upper radiator hose to collapse as the system cools down. Check the vacuum valve by pulling it gently and verifying the slight spring tension.

Fig. 3-6. *Pressure-test the cooling system to locate leakage.*

Finally, with the engine running, listen for noises:

- Engine thump at normal operating temperature could indicate a restriction in coolant flow
- Screeching could indicate a loose accessory drive belt or failing water pump bearing
- Buzz or whistle could indicate a poor pressure cap seal or vibrating fan shroud
- Ringing or grinding noise could indicate a worn or damaged water pump bearing, loose drive belt pulley, or defective belt tensioner pulley bearing
- Gurgling from the radiator could indicate a plugged radiator or air in the coolant

System Leak Check

The quickest way to find an external coolant leak is by pressure-testing the cooling system, figure 3-6. Perform the test on a cold engine using a hand pump with a gauge as follows:

1. Remove the pressure cap and attach the tester to the filler neck.
2. Pump the tester until the gauge reading matches the specified system pressure.
3. Ensure the gauge reading remains steady.
4. If the gauge shows a pressure loss, pump the tester to maintain pressure and check for leaks. External leaks should be obvious as pressure in the system forces the coolant out.
5. If no sign of leakage is found, the leak is internal and additional testing is required.

Internal coolant leaks, generally the result of head gasket failure or casting cracks, are more difficult to detect.

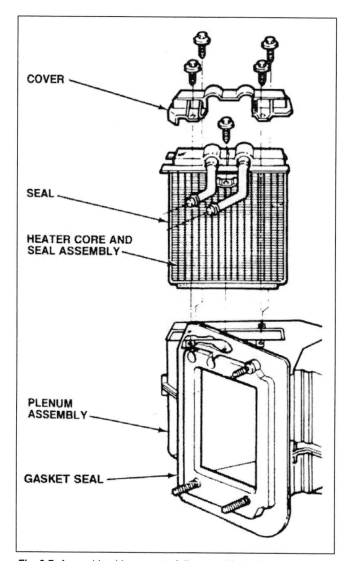

Fig. 3-7. *A considerable amount of disassembly is often required to remove the heater core from the plenum assembly.*

Coolant may be seeping into either the combustion chambers or the crankcase. To check for leakage into the crankcase, remove the dipstick. If the oil on the dipstick looks milky or thickened, it may be contaminated by leaking coolant.

There are several methods to check for coolant in the combustion chambers. Remove the radiator cap, start the engine, and bring it to operating temperature. A major leak reveals itself by creating bubbles in the coolant that rise to the surface at the filler neck. Small leaks can be detected using a chemical test kit or an exhaust gas analyzer.

With chemical testing, vapors directly above the coolant in the radiator are passed through a liquid sensitive to exhaust gases. To use an exhaust gas analyzer, hold the wand over the filler neck. Never allow coolant to be drawn into the machine. Any exhaust gases in the system register on the meters.

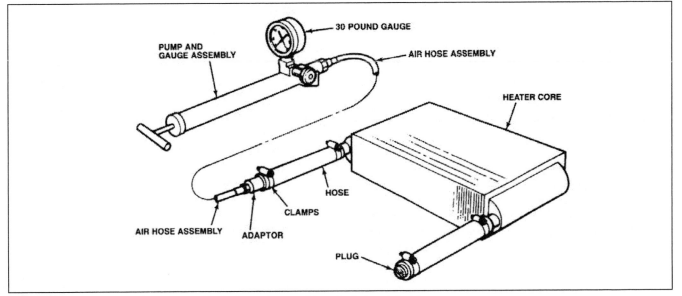

Fig. 3-8. Seal and charge a heater core with air, then submerge it in water to bench-test it.

Pressure test and inspect the coolant system before draining. Drain the system completely by opening the petcock at the bottom of the radiator and the plugs in the engine block. If the coolant is dirty, or there are deposits in the radiator, flush the cooling system before refilling.

Various methods and equipment may be used to flush the system. If using equipment such as a back flusher, follow the manufacturer's instructions. However, the thermostat should be removed before flushing the system.

Disconnect all hoses from the coolant reservoir. Remove the reservoir and pour out any fluid. Scrub the inside of reservoir with soap and water. Flush it well with clean water, and then drain it. Install the reservoir and hoses. Install the thermostat, close the radiator petcock and engine block drains. Refill the cooling system with coolant meeting OEM's specifications. To ensure sufficient engine cooling, freezing and engine corrosion protection, maintain a 50/50 solution of water and antifreeze. This will achieve a protection level of -34°F (-37°C). Never use a solution that is more than 70% antifreeze.

Fill the radiator or coolant fill pipe to the base of the filler neck. Fill the coolant reservoir to the "FULL HOT" mark. Before replacing the pressure cap, test it as described earlier in this chapter. Start and run the engine with the pressure cap removed, until the upper radiator hose is hot. With the engine idling, add coolant to the radiator until it reaches the bottom of the filler neck. Install the pressure cap making sure the cap is secure. Allow the engine to cool to ambient temperature, then check the coolant in the reservoir rank. If not at the "FULL COLD" mark, add coolant.

HEATER CORE SERVICE

Many problems with the heating system are caused by heater core failure. Service procedures include:

- Pressure testing
- Bench testing
- Flushing

Pressure Test

If the engine coolant level is low but the cooling system is not leaking, check the heater core. Coolant may leak from pinholes in the heater core in the form of steam, which enters the passenger compartment along with the heated air. When this air condenses against the cold windows, the coolant deposits there, forming a sticky, sweet-smelling residue. To pressure-test the heater core on the vehicle:

1. Drain the coolant.
2. Disconnect the heater hoses from the heater core inlet and outlet tubes.
3. Use adapters to connect a cooling system pressure tester to one heater core tube.
4. Fill the heater core with water and seal off the other tube.
5. Apply specified pressure with the hand pump and watch the gauge for at least three minutes:
   - If pressure holds for three minutes, the heater core is not leaking
   - If the pressure drops, double-check the connection between the tester and heater core; if the leak is not there, remove the heater core for bench testing

Bench Test

Removing the heater core from the vehicle may require considerable disassembly of the heating, ventilation, and air conditioning system plenum or ductwork, figure 3-7. Once removed, bench-test the core to locate the leak:

1. Drain the coolant and plug one heater core tube with a suitable stopper.
2. Seal the other tube using a fitting with an air valve.
3. Use a hand pump or low-pressure compressed air and charge heater core to the recommended pressure, figure 3-8.
4. Submerge the pressurized heater core in a water bath and watch for a stream of bubbles from the leak.

Some heater cores can be repaired by a radiator shop while others must be replaced if a leak is found.

Flushing

A heater core can collect sediment or scale that insulates the heater core metal from the coolant and reduces the amount of heat available for the passenger compartment. Backflushing, which sends water through the heater core in the opposite direction from the normal coolant flow, removes this sediment without removing the heater core from the vehicle. To backflush:

1. Remove the heater hoses.
2. Connect a drain hose to the inlet tube.
3. Attach a hose and nozzle to the outlet and spray pressurized water through the heater core.

Chemicals such as oxalic acid can also remove deposits. The acid breaks up oily, scaly deposits in the system that water cannot dissolve.

1. Possible causes of the heater not providing any heat at all include all of the following, *EXCEPT*:
   a. High current flow to blower
   b. Blocked coolant flow through heater core
   c. Blocked air inlet ducts
   d. Clogged heater hoses

2. Very little airflow into the passenger compartment can be caused by all of the following, *EXCEPT*:
   a. A partially blocked cowl intake vent
   b. A normal condition at low vehicle speeds
   c. An open circuit to the fan motor
   d. An intake air door jammed shut

3. A heater control valve may be operated by:
   a. Hydraulic pressure
   b. Mechanical crank
   c. Engine-run pulley
   d. Vacuum actuator

4. An upper radiator hose that collapses as the engine cooling system cools down is most likely caused by:
   a. Plugged or damaged radiator fins
   b. A defective radiator cap
   c. Restricted coolant flow
   d. A plugged water pump vent

5. What is the most likely cause of a heating system that fogs the windshield and leaves an oily film on the inside of the glass?
   a. Air or coolant leak in the heater plenum
   b. Debris in the ram air intake system
   c. A leaking heater control valve
   d. Intake air doors stuck closed

6. A grinding noise from the accessory drive belts can be caused by all of the following, *EXCEPT*:
   a. A damaged water pump bearing
   b. A defective belt tensioner pulley bearing
   c. A glazed, cracked or broken drive belt
   d. A binding A/C belt idler pulley bearing

7. To pressure-test a heater core:
   a. Top off the coolant
   b. Use a special pressure tester
   c. Run the engine
   d. Set the heater control on high

8. A heater core has had sediment buildup; to remove it by backflushing:
   a. Remove the heater core from the plenum
   b. Soak the core in a chemical flush to loosen deposits
   c. Run water through the heater core outlet
   d. Pressurize the heater core with air

Chapter Four

OPERATING SYSTEMS AND RELATED CONTROLS DIAGNOSIS AND REPAIR

HVAC systems rely on either mechanical, vacuum, electric, electronic controls, or various combinations of these four methods, to regulate the temperature and distribution of the airflow into the passenger compartment.

MECHANICAL OPERATING CONTROLS

Mechanical controls are simple, cable-operated devices that move levers or rotary switches to pull **blend doors** and **mode doors** into position, figure 4-1. The blend door determines how much of the intake air is directed through the heater core before entering the passenger compartment. Mode doors direct the airflow to the various ducts. An incorrectly positioned door cannot deliver the proper airflow. Blend and mode door position problems may be caused by the doors themselves binding, being blocked by debris, or by a control cable that is out of adjustment, kinked, loose, or broken. Most newer control cables have a self-adjusting clip, but the self-adjustment range is limited. Adjust control cables before installation:

1. Insert a small screwdriver into the control cable wire loop at the end of the blend door crank arm.
2. Use pliers to slide the self-adjusting clip about one inch (25 mm) down the control cable and away from the end loop, figure 4-2.
3. Set the temperature control lever at maximum cool, then snap the cable housing into the mounting bracket.
4. Attach the self-adjusting clip to the temperature door crank arm.
5. Move the temperature control lever to maximum heat, position the self-adjusting clip, and check cable operation.

VACUUM-OPERATED CONTROLS

Vacuum-operated climate-control systems use intake manifold **vacuum** to operate controls and **actuators**. Many vacuum systems are complex, so it is important to have a vacuum diagram and specifications for the specific vehicle being serviced. In general, take vacu-

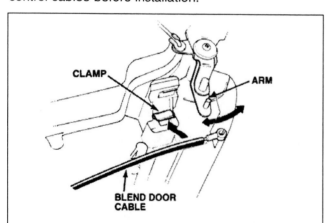

Fig. 4-1. Mechanical controls use a cable assembly to position the blend door.

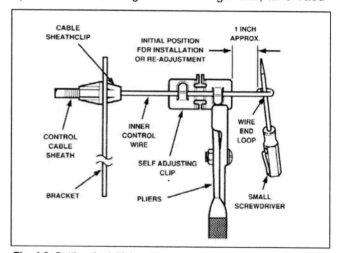

Fig. 4-2. Setting the initial position on a new self-adjusting control cable.

Actuator: A component that converts a vacuum or electrical signal into a physical movement, to operate a part such as a blend door or valve.

Blend Door: A door in an HVAC system that directs air through or around the heater core.

Mode Door: A door in an HVAC system that directs air to the defrost, dash, and heat ducts.

Vacuum: A pressure less than atmospheric pressure.

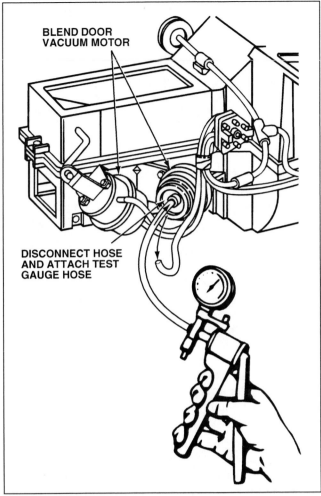

BLEND DOOR
VACUUM MOTOR

DISCONNECT HOSE
AND ATTACH TEST
GAUGE HOSE

Fig. 4-3. Testing a vacuum operated blend door actuator.

um readings at engine idle speed using a vacuum gauge. Often, components can be tested without removing them from the vehicle using a hand-operated vacuum pump.

Vacuum Component Diagnosis and Replacement

Be aware, moving vacuum-controlled blend doors manually can damage the vacuum motor diaphragm. Disconnect the doors from the actuators before testing door movement. Universal replacement vacuum motors, which have an adjustable actuating rod allowing them to be used on a number of vehicles, are readily available. To test the vacuum actuator:

1. Connect a vacuum pump to the diaphragm inlet port and apply about 15 to 20 in-Hg (350 to 500 mm-Hg) of vacuum, figure 4-3.
2. Check diaphragm plunger or linkage operation in all positions.
3. Close the pump shutoff valve and watch the gauge. The readings should hold steady for at least one minute if the diaphragm is not leaking.

4. Repeat for each inlet port in the vacuum motor.
5. Be sure the door moves when vacuum is applied.

Troubleshooting the Vacuum System

Begin with a visual inspection:

1. Check vacuum hose routing and connections. Look for and straighten or replace pinched, kinked, or damaged vacuum lines or hoses.
2. Check for blend door interference, disconnect the vacuum servo and check for full travel and free door movement.
3. Check the temperature control cable for kinks, binding, or improper routing.
4. Check all linkages for binding, damage, or loose connections.
5. Connect a vacuum pump to one port of the vacuum reservoir, plug the other port when applicable. Apply 15 to 20 in-Hg of vacuum. The reservoir should hold the vacuum for 5 minutes. If it leaks, replace the reservoir.
6. Connect a vacuum pump to one side of a check valve, the valve should hold 15-20 in-Hg of vacuum, then connect the pump to the opposite end of the valve, apply vacuum, the valve should allow a free flow in one direction only.
7. Check restrictor valves by applying vacuum to either side. The valve should bleed down vacuum quickly and smoothly.

Many automatic and semi-automatic temperature control systems use electronically actuated vacuum motors to position blend doors and mode doors. Blend doors to maintain a constant temperature in the passenger compartment by mixing fresh or recirculated air with heated or cooled air, figure 4-4. Mode doors direct air flow to the various defrost, dash, and heat ducts. When diagnosing vacuum motors, thoroughly evaluate the vacuum system before attempting to repair the electronic controls. To check blend and mode door operation:

1. Remove the glove box or other obstructions to gain a clear view of the blend door linkage and motor.
2. Start and run the engine until the upper radiator hose feels warm to the touch. Then, move the mode selector to NORM and switch the blower control to HIGH.
3. Move the temperature selection lever from warm to cold while watching the blend door mechanism. Once the blend door moves to the full cold position, move the selector to the full hot setting. Air temperature from the ducts should change as the system adjusts the blend door position.

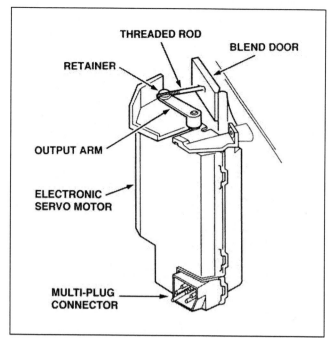

Fig. 4-4. *Automatic and semi-automatic temperature control systems often use electronic solenoids to operate the blend door vacuum motors.*

4. Move the mode selector lever through all available modes. The air should flow from the appropriate heat, defrost, and dash ducts.

If the air temperature or flow does not change, refer to the appropriate section below.

Manual Controls

- Check and adjust the temperature control cable as needed and retest
- Check the vacuum motor linkage and adjust or repair as needed
- If the door moves freely, but only cold air is distributed through the system, check for vacuum at the heater control valve. Vacuum should not be present unless the system is in the MAX A/C setting

Automatic and Semi-Automatic Controls

- Check the blend door movement when the controls are changed from hot to cold. If there is no movement, or it is insufficient, separate the blend door lever or rod from the actuator assembly and check that the door moves freely through its full travel
- If the door moves freely, but is not being moved by the programmer, the problem is in the controls
- If there is sufficient blend door movement, but only cold air is distributed through the system, check for vacuum at the heater control valve. Vacuum should not be present unless the system is in the MAX A/C setting
- If hot coolant is available to the heater core, but only cold air is distributed, either coolant is not cir-

culating through the heater core or air is not flowing through the heater. Feel the heater core return hose to check for circulation

Testing control problems begins with a vacuum and wiring diagram, and a knowledge of how the system is supposed to work. A few basic rules apply to testing manual, automatic, and semi-automatic temperature control systems.

If the discharge air is too cold, check for:

1. Insufficient hot coolant circulating through the heater core.
2. Insufficient airflow through the heater core.

If the discharge air is too hot, check for:

1. Excessive hot coolant circulation through the heater core.
2. Too much airflow being directed through the heater core.

ELECTRICAL AND ELECTRONIC CONTROLS

Electrical and electronic diagnosis is an organized procedure using information and testing to find the cause of a failure. The four basic steps are:

1. Verify the complaint, research the problem, and determine which specific components may be the cause of the complaint.
2. Find the affected circuit on the electrical schematic or wiring diagram.
3. Locate common points of power supply and ground to the branch circuits.
4. Do an area test of the branch circuit using various electrical tests to pinpoint the problem.

This procedure is especially useful in tracing power supply problems to individual components. Electronic control systems use low-voltage signals, so connection quality is even more important. Where possible, use trouble code readouts to localize the problem to specific circuits.

Electrical Circuits and Components

Direct Current (DC) circuits receive current at one end and connect to ground at the other, so the most logical test is to start at one end of the circuit and work your way to the other. Keep in mind:

- If one component, such as an actuator motor, is defective in a circuit with many parts, start the test at the defective part
- If all the parts in the circuit are not operating properly, check ground, then check along the circuit, starting at the power source

In complex, electronically controlled systems, test one sub-system at a time to narrow the problem down to a specific area. Then, perform more detailed tests to isolate the faulty component.

Servicing Electronic Control Systems

Most electronic control systems have a dedicated Electronic Control Module (ECM) for the climate control system. Typically, the climate control ECM is located behind the **control head**, although some may be located along side, or incorporated into, the Body Control Module (BCM). Consult the service manual to locate the control module.

Most electronic systems have onboard diagnostic programs that are capable of performing self-test routines and storing a Diagnostic Trouble Code (DTC) when a malfunction occurs. Use a scan tool and follow service manual for the exact year, model, and type of climate control system being serviced to access the onboard diagnostic programs.

Self-diagnostic procedures and diagnostic trouble codes seldom reveal the exact nature of a failure. However, they do narrow the problem area and indicate where to begin pinpoint testing. Once the problem has been repaired, rerun the self-diagnostic program to ensure that the fault has been corrected and the system is functioning properly.

Present day vehicles rely on the PCM to command the A/C compressor either on or off. When the PCM receives an HVAC request requiring compressor clutch engagement, the PCM will modify the engine RPM to minimize the impact of compressor clutch operation on engine idle speed.

Some of the PCM inputs are as follows:

- Power steering cutout switch
- Engine Coolant Temperature (ECT)
- Engine RPM
- Ambient Air Temperature (AAT)
- Intake Air Temperature (IAT)
- Vehicle Speed Sensor (VSS)
- Low refrigerant pressure switch
- A/C high-side pressure
- A/C low-side pressure
- Throttle Position (TP) Sensor

Because of the PCM's role in most HVAC systems today, testing and repair require the use of the appropriate scan tool as described in this chapter.

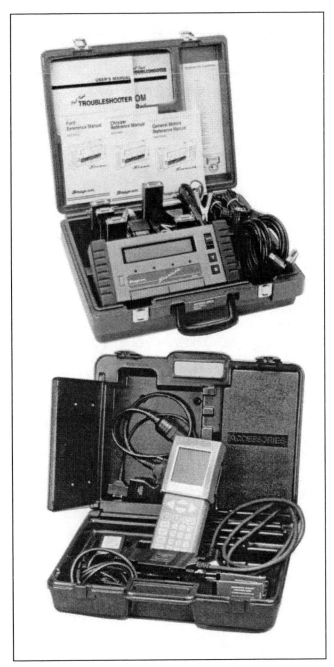

Fig. 4-5. *A scan tool is the only electronic tester that permits direct communication with the onboard computer.*

Special Testers

Various special electronic testers have been developed to simplify troubleshooting electronic control systems. Although these testers are helpful, they do not repair system failures. A thorough understanding of the test procedures and system operations are required to accurately interpret the results of tests.

Control Head: The dashboard-mounted unit that contains the controls for the HVAC systems.

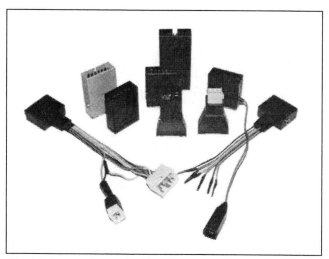

Fig. 4-6. *An assortment of cable adapters provides access to a number of onboard control systems.*

Onboard Diagnostic Communication

Most late-model vehicles have a diagnostic connectors, or Data Link Connector (DLC) that allows the onboard computer to communicate with a scan tool or other diagnostic test equipment. The DLC may be located in the engine compartment of earlier vehicles, and some models use a dedicated connector that only accesses the A/C or climate control system. Late-model vehicles that comply with OBD-II regulations communicate through the 16-pin DLC located in the passenger compartment.

Scan Tool Capabilities

A scan tool is a hand-held computer that is capable of communicating with the onboard computers of a vehicle, figure 4-5. Scan tools are the only diagnostic tool that will display internal control module information. All other electronic test instruments are limited to accessing the external input and output circuits. A quality scan tool provides:

- DTC retrieval
- Access to the data stream
- The ability to record data during a road test
- A means to actuate onboard tests

The information the vehicle communicates to the scan tool is a function of the onboard computer, not the scan tool. Most vehicle manufacturers market scan tools designed specifically for servicing their systems. Aftermarket scan tools are also available from a number of vendors. Interchangeable software cartridges and cable connectors adapt an aftermarket scan tool to different control system designs, figure 4-6.

A scan tool is essential for diagnosing problems in the electronic control system. The latest units provide a great deal of valuable diagnostic information that is difficult, or impossible, to obtain any other way. Because a scan tool is portable, it can be used while road testing the vehicle. Watching "live" data provides the opportunity to catch an intermittent problem. One of the most useful features of a scan tool is its ability to record data during a road test for play back at a later time. These recordings are called snapshots, movies, or events by the various scan tool manufacturers. When viewing a recording, data appears as if it were live, but permits viewing of sensor and actuator activity at a relaxed pace.

Electrical and Electronic Component Service

All HVAC systems have an electric blower motor, compressor clutch, and may have control of the engine cooling fan(s) as well. Some systems use electric servo motors to position the blend and mode doors. Any or all of these electric motors may be controlled by the temperature control computer. Automatic and semi-automatic systems use a number of sensors and actuators to maintain a preset passenger compartment temperature. As discussed previously, the PCM uses electronic engine data inputs to make decisions when to command A/C clutch operation. The PCM also controls

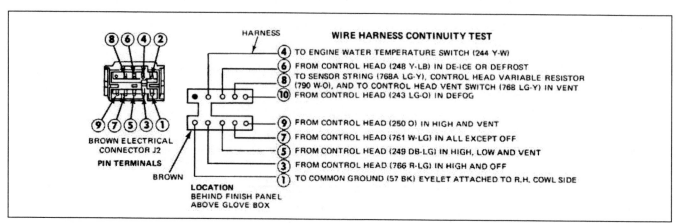

Fig. 4-7. *A pin-out chart is needed to check blower switch circuits.*

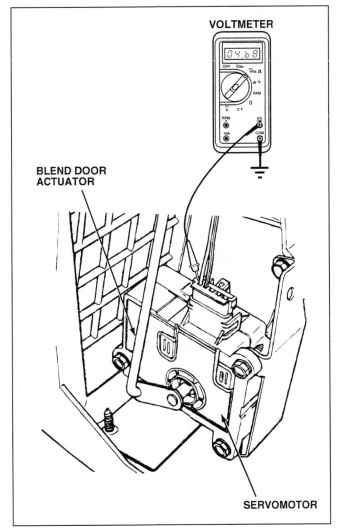

Fig. 4-8. Check for system voltage, usually about 5 volts on an electronic system, available at the servomotor.

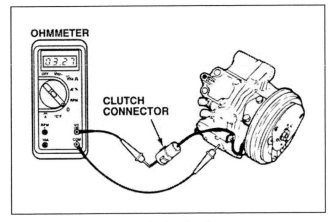

Fig. 4-9. Check compressor clutch coil resistance.

engine RPM during A/C operation. The devices related to the A/C operation also supply inputs used to control engine-cooling fans.

WARNING: Keep hands, tools and clothing away from the engine cooling fan(s) to help prevent personal injury. The fan can start automatically in response to a PCM command whether or not the engine is running.

Blower Motor

Most ATC HVAC systems utilize a system to control blower operation until the engine reaches operating temperature. Whenever the HVAC system is turned on in any mode, except defog, and the coolant temperature is below approximately 28°F (-2C°), blower operation is disabled. During this time the blower will be commanded off, any airflow will be directed to the front defrost outlets to keep moisture off the windshield.

Normal blower operation resumes when the defrost function is selected or after the coolant temperature reaches approximately 110°F (43°C).

The blower motor circuit includes the motor, switch, and wiring harness that links them together. Refer to the service manual for specific test information.

Test switch continuity with an ohmmeter, following the procedures outlined in the appropriate service manual.

Many vehicles are equipped with a blower motor resistor block, figure 4-7. The resistor block is serviced only as an assembly, if found to be defective.

Many late-model vehicles control blower motor speed with the use of an electronic control module. This control module provides an output voltage to the blower motor proportional to the control switch position.

Diagnosis of the blower motor control module can normally be accomplished with the use of the proper scan tool.

Blend and Mode Door Servomotors

Do not move blend or mode doors manually, as this may cause damage. Blend and mode doors can be repositioned through an onboard diagnostic program with a scan tool on some systems. On other systems, sensors may need to be disconnected or harness terminals jumpered to move the blend doors. Refer to the appropriate service manual for moving the blend and mode doors to check alignment in all positions.

An electronically controlled, high-torque servomotor normally produces a low, humming sound as the blend door moves. If the servomotor does not move, check for proper voltage to the servomotor and for proper grounding, figure 4-8. If voltage is available, but the servomotor does not rotate, check for obstructions at the blend or mode door or binding in the linkage before condemning the motor.

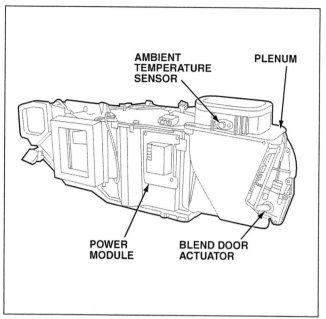

Fig. 4-10 *The ambient temperature sensor measures HVAC system intake air temperature.*

Compressor Clutch

The compressor clutch is an electromagnetic device that mechanically connects the compressor pulley to the compressor input shaft. Electrical or component failures that may prevent clutch engagement include:

- Safety switches
  - Refrigerant pressure
  - Coolant temperature
- PCM commands based on inputs from:
  - Power Steering Pressure (PSP) sensor
  - Throttle Position (TP) Sensor
  - Engine Coolant Temperature (ECT)
- Time-delay relay
- Blown fuses
- Open electrical connections or wiring
- Defective clutch relay
- Defective A/C module

Check clutch operation by moving the mode selector between the OFF and MAX A/C positions with the engine running. You should hear a click and momentary change in engine speed every time the clutch engages or disengages. If the clutch is not engaging:

1. With the engine running and A/C switched on, test

both clutch coil electrical connections with a voltmeter. The possibilities are:

- Zero volts at either terminal indicates no available voltage to the clutch
- 12 volts at both terminals indicates the potential of an open ground circuit
- 12 volts on one terminal and zero volts on the other indicates an open in the compressor clutch coil

2. If a faulty clutch coil is indicated, check coil resistance with an ohmmeter, figure 4-9. Typical clutch coil resistance should be 3-5 ohms.
3. Another possibility is high resistance in either the power or ground circuit. High resistance in the power circuit results in less than required current flow to the clutch coil. Refer to the appropriate service manual for specific circuit tests.
4. Once the fault is isolated to power or ground side of the clutch circuit, check the switches by momentarily jumping each switch or connection that may be preventing clutch operation. If clutch operation is restored when you jump a switch, investigate the reason for the open switch.

Caution: Never jump across a sensor as damage to the PCM or other electronic controls may result.

Never operate the system for more than 60 seconds with a jumper wire installed on a switch. The switch may be functioning properly and opened due to a problem in the system, such as an extremely low refrigerant level, and operating the system can cause compressor damage.

Temperature Switches and Sensors

Temperature switches such as the **ambient temperature switch** and the engine **coolant temperature switch** are on/off devices that control circuits based on temperature.

Most late-model vehicles have replace temperature switches with temperature sensors. These sensors are generally thermistors, and are used to provide input to various control modules. A typical system uses thermistors to monitor the **ambient temperature**, evaporator temperature, coolant temperature, and passenger compartment temperature.

An additional coolant temperature switch or sensor may be used to operate an electric cooling fan.

Ambient Temperature: The temperature of the air surrounding a component.

Ambient Temperature Switch: A digital on/off device that senses ambient temperature and switches off the A/C compressor when the temperature is too cold.

Coolant Temperature Switch: A digital on/off device that senses engine coolant temperature and switches off the A/C compressor when the temperature is too hot, reducing engine load.

TEMPERATURE		SENSOR
F	(C)	VOLTAGE
248	(120)	0.25
212	(100)	0.46
176	(80)	0.84
150	(66)	1.34
140	(60)	1.55
104	(40)	2.27
86	(30)	2.60
68	(20)	2.93
32	(0)	3.59
-4	(-20)	4.24
-40	(-40)	4.90

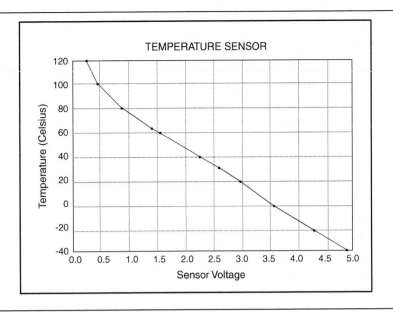

Fig. 4-11. Manufacturers include specifications for temperature sensor voltage drop testing.

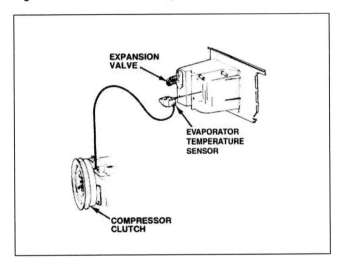

Fig. 4-12. An evaporator temperature sensor is a thermostatic switch that prevents compressor engagement if the evaporator freezes.

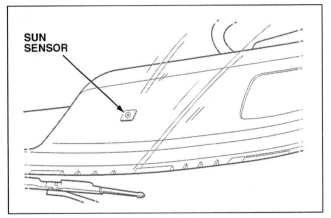

Fig. 4-13. The sun sensor is a photo diode that responds to the intensity of sunlight.

The ambient temperature switch transmits HVAC intake air temperature as a voltage signal to the control module to open and close the compressor clutch circuit, figure 4-10. The switch is generally mounted either in the plenum or near the radiator support. A typical ambient temperature switch opens the compressor clutch circuit to prevent compressor operation below about 35°F (2°C), and closes to allow normal compressor operation at temperatures of about 50°F (10°C) or above.

An **ambient temperature sensor** is an electronic device that transmits a variable voltage signal to the control unit. The resistance of an ambient sensor varies in proportion to temperature changes. In addition to controlling compressor clutch operation, an ambient temperature sensor signal may also be used by the control unit to compute the correct blend door position.

Whether the system uses a switch or sensor, check the service manual for test conditions and specifications. Either device can be tested with an ohmmeter. To check:

1. With the ignition off, disconnect the A/C control head.
2. Measure the resistance between the two terminals. If it is:

   • Within specifications, the switch is functioning

Ambient Temperature Sensor: An electronic device that transmits a variable voltage signal based on temperature. Sensor resistance varies with temperature changes.

normally
- Infinite, check the wiring for an open circuit between the sensor and the control head
- If resistance differs considerably from specifications, replace the sensor

A more accurate method of checking a temperature sensor and circuit operation is by voltage drop testing. The resistance of the thermistor, which varies with temperature, determines how much of a reference voltage, usually 5 volts, is dropped by the sensor. Take readings and compare to service manual specifications, figure 4-11. Thermistors are typically designed to operate near the mid-point of their range under normal conditions, so expect up to about 2.5 volts on a 5-volt circuit when air temperature is about 86°F (30°C).

An evaporator temperature thermostatic switch, which prevents compressor engagement if the evaporator gets too cold, can be the source of an apparent compressor clutch failure, figure 4-12. If this switch fails, the clutch may:

- Not engage because the switch does not open
- Fail to cycle because the switch does not close
- Cycle erratically

Check internal resistance of the evaporator temperature switch, and all other thermistors that are used in the system, with an ohmmeter. Check sensor and circuit performance by voltage drop testing. Consult the appropriate service manual for procedures and specifications.

Sun Sensor

Automatic and semi-automatic temperature control systems often have a sun sensor, which is used to adjust blend door position depending upon the intensity of the sunlight. A sun sensor generally installs on the top of the dash panel and uses a light-sensitive photo diode to vary circuit resistance through the device, figure 4-13. Perform resistance and voltage drop tests. Replace the sensor if it is defective.

Servicing the Automatic Control Panel

If the control panel of an automatic temperature control system fails, replace it. Some typical control panel failures include sticking or non-functioning push buttons, or lack of display illumination. Another sign is if the computer does not remember comfort settings when the vehicle is turned off and restarted.

1. Most cable-type HVAC controls are:
   a. Adjustable
   b. Self-adjusting
   c. Nonadjustable
   d. Obsolete

2. The most likely cause for temperature controller malfunction in a vacuum-operated HVAC system is a problem with the:
   a. Vacuum system
   b. Engine cooling system
   c. Electrical system
   d. Engine manifold

3. The most likely cause of the heater distributing only cold air when hot engine coolant is available at the heater core on a vacuum-operated HVAC system would be:
   a. No vacuum to the programmer checking relay
   b. A defective vacuum servo
   c. An incorrectly adjusted cable
   d. An open blend door actuator circuit

4. Most electronic climate-control modules are located:
   a. In the engine compartment
   b. In the trunk
   c. Under the driver's seat
   d. Behind the control head

5. A thermistor-type sensor can be used on a climate control system for all of the following **EXCEPT**:
   a. Evaporator temperature switch
   b. Ambient temperature switch
   c. Sun sensor
   d. Coolant temperature sensor

6. The onboard diagnostic program of a computer-controlled HVAC system can provide all of the following **EXCEPT**:
   a. Diagnostic trouble codes
   b. Serial data access
   c. Functional tests
   d. Pinpoint test results

7. The only tool capable of displaying internal control module information is a:
   a. Digital Multimeter (DMM)
   b. Scan tool
   c. Special system tester
   d. Lab scope

8. The most accurate method of checking a temperature sensor and circuit is by:
   a. Accessing the data stream
   b. Checking resistance with an ohmmeter
   c. Voltage drop testing
   d. Scan tool testing

9. If clutch coil resistance is within specifications, check engagement by:
   a. Connecting the coil to battery power with jump wires
   b. Installing a jump wire across the relay
   c. Measuring available voltage with the control panel set to maximum cool
   d. Grounding the clutch coil circuit

10. An evaporator temperature thermostatic switch is used to:
    a. Regulate refrigerant flow through the evaporator
    b. Prevent compressor operation above a certain ambient temperature
    c. Prevent compressor operation if refrigerant level is too low
    d. Prevent compressor engagement if the evaporator is too cold

Chapter Five

REFRIGERANT RECOVERY, RECYCLING, HANDLING, AND RETROFIT

RECOVERY AND RECYCLING EQUIPMENT

Recovery and recycling stations capture, filter, and store the refrigerant evacuated from a system for reuse. Typically, recycling salvages about 65 percent of the refrigerant charge. Recovery and recycling stations are available for R-12 and R-134a refrigerants. Dual stations are available that can process both R-12 and R-134a. However, these are two units combined into one cabinet, and a single station cannot process both types of refrigerant. Mixing R-12 with R-134a, or any other refrigerant blend, contaminates the recycling station and results in costly repairs. Use a refrigerant identifier to verify what refrigerant is in the system being serviced before hooking up service equipment.

Maintenance and Certification

The Federal Clean Air Act, Section 609, requires that anyone who performs a service involving refrigerant on an automotive A/C system must be certified to do so. Certification forms can be obtained from the manufacturers of UL-approved refrigerant recovery/recycling equipment. The equipment should have a label saying it is UL-approved and meets SAE standard J1991.

To qualify for certification, a shop must have UL-approved recovery and recycling equipment, and the technician must be able to show proof of training on the use and maintenance of the equipment. The certification form requires the equipment serial number and the signature of the equipment owner or a responsible officer, in addition to the name and address of the technician. Remember that without this certification, it is illegal to perform any refrigerant service.

The Society of Automotive Engineers (SAE) established three standards, J1989, J1990, and J1991, concerning refrigerant recycling, which the U.S. government incorporated into laws. Recycled R-12 is defined by SAE Standard J1991, and manufacturers must make sure their equipment meets this standard, and all applicable recycling equipment standards.

Standard J1990 also applies to equipment manufacture, but contains guidelines that technicians should be aware of, such as the requirement that the tank be tested every five years. This standard also specifies that service hose shutoff valves must be within 12 inches of the hose ends to prevent unnecessary refrigerant release. The equipment must also be able to separate refrigeration oil that comes out of a system during refrigerant discharge and be able to indicate the amount of oil lost, so the technician can replace it in the system. Standard J1989 applies directly to the service technician, establishing guidelines for recovery and recycling equipment use.

Refrigerant Recovery

A recovery and recycling station connects to the vehicle through a manifold gauge set or a charging station, figure 5-1. Once the vehicle system has been serviced, the refrigerant remaining in the manifold gauge set or charging station hoses must be recovered before the service ports are disconnected. Before recovery, connect a manifold gauge set, and verify that there is pressure in the system. Observe all safety precautions and equipment operating procedures detailed in certification training. To recover refrigerant:

1. With the manifold gauge set connected to the vehicle, attach the center hose to the intake side of the recovery and recycling station.
2. Make sure the liquid valves of the recovery station are open, then open both manifold gauge valves.
3. Switch the power on and start the recovery station compressor. The compressor automatically switches off once recovery is complete.
4. Monitor manifold gauges for several minutes, if pressure on either side rises above zero, repeat step 3.
5. Open the recovery station oil drain valve until all oil removed from the system drains from the separator.
6. Note the amount of oil in the catch and add that much fresh oil to the system before recharging.

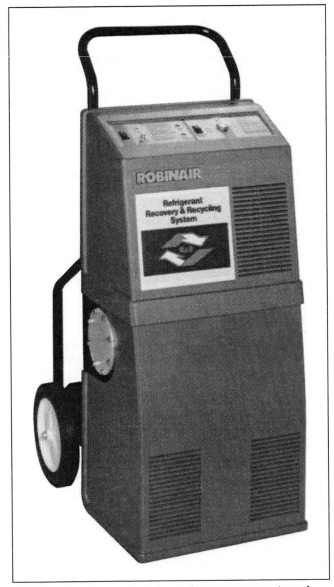

Fig. 5-1. *A recovery and recycling station processes one type of refrigerant for reuse.*

Refrigerant Recycling

There are two types of recycling equipment: single-pass and multi-pass. Single-pass equipment sends the refrigerant through each recycling stage one time before storing it for use, figure 5-2. A multi-pass system may not complete all the recycling stages before storing the refrigerant, figure 5-3. When refrigerant is needed to charge a system, the equipment cycles the refrigerant until it is clean and dry enough to meet standards for reuse. Either type of system can be used as long as it is UL-approved.

Recycling removes moisture and non-condensable gases from used refrigerant so that it conforms to purity standards established by SAE J1991. For best results and efficiency, the recovery and recycling sta-

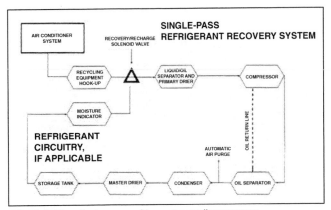

Fig. 5-2. *The single-pass refrigerant recycling process.*

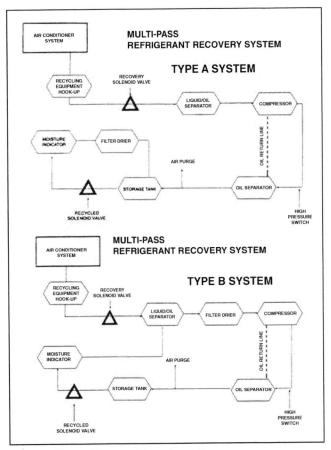

Fig. 5-3. *The multi-pass refrigerant recycling process.*

tion recovery tank should be full before recycling. Recycling operations vary slightly by equipment; the following is a general procedure:

1. Open both recovery tank valves on the recovery and recycling station.
2. Switch the station power on and activate the switch that starts the recycle operation.
3. Use the station moisture indicator as a sight glass; expect to see a stream of bubbles at start-up that quickly dissipates to no bubbles as the pump reaches peak efficiency.

Fig. 5-4. A refrigerant identifier determines the type of refrigerant in a system.

4. Run the pump at peak efficiency for at least 30 minutes, then check the moisture indicator. Severely contaminated refrigerant can take several hours to recycle. Monitor the moisture indicator and switch the pump off once the refrigerant meets SAE standards.
5. Switch the station power off and close both recovery tank valves.

Disconnect, label, and store the recycled refrigerant tank according to regulations.

REFRIGERANT

In addition to purity standards for recycled refrigerant, SAE standards apply to refrigerant identification, handling, labeling, and storage. Follow all applicable rules as detailed in certification training.

Identification

Read all labels before using a container of refrigerant to make sure it is the correct type for the system being serviced. Use a refrigerant identifier to determine what the vehicle system is charged with; this prevents equipment contamination, figure 5-4. New containers of R-12 are painted white, while R-134a containers are blue. Observe the same color coding when recycling. Remember: Never put R-12 into an R-134a system, or vice versa, or contaminate equipment with another blend of refrigerant.

Handling

Never vent R-12 or R-134a into the air. Always use a recovery and recycling system. Follow the equipment instructions when using recovery and recycling equipment to be within the legal requirements. Separate

recovery and recycling equipment, manifold gauges, replacement parts, and leak detectors are required for R-12 and R-134a systems.

Labeling and Storage

The storage containers for recycled R-12 must qualify for DOT CFR Title 49. Such a container has "DOT4BA" or "DOT4BW" stamped on it. Never put refrigerant into a disposable container. Before transferring refrigerant into a DOT-approved container, evacuate the tank to at least 17 in-Hg (75 mm-Hg). Find the container gross weight rating and fill it to only 60 percent of that rating. For example, put 30 pounds of refrigerant into a 50-pound container. To dispose of an empty container, evacuate it using approved recovery and recycling equipment until it shows vacuum. Write the word "empty" on the container and dispose of it according to local regulations.

Testing Recycled Refrigerant

Before using recycled refrigerant that has been stored in a portable container, check for non-condensable gases, or air, in the tank. This is an extremely important step that must not be overlooked. To check for non-condensable gases:

1. Store the container at 65° F (18.3° C), out of direct sunlight, for at least 12 hours before testing. Use a reliable thermometer to monitor ambient temperature within 4 inches (10 cm) of the container.
2. Connect a pressure gauge that measures in 1-psi (0.1 kg/cm2) increments to the refrigerant container.
3. Compare gauge readings with a pressure and temperature chart, figure 5-5. If the refrigerant pressure is:
   - At or below the specified pressure, the refrigerant can be used
   - Above the specified pressure, continue by purging the tank
4. Attach the recovery and recycling station to the container and slowly vent vapor until the pressure drops below the specified limit. If necessary, recycle the container contents.

R-134a RETROFIT

Retrofit to R-134a should always be considered as an option anytime an R-12 A/C system requires major repairs. This includes any R-12 system that needs a replacement compressor, condenser, evaporator or maybe even hoses. In such situations, you can save your customer much of what it would cost to retrofit later by going ahead and doing the conversion now.

PRESSURE/TEMPERATURE CHART

DEGREES F/C	PRESSURE PSI/Bar	DEGREES F/C	PRESSURE PSI/Bar	DEGREES F/C	PRESSURE PSI/Bar	DEGREES F/C	PRESSURE PSI/Bar	DEGREES F/C	PRESSURE PSI/Bar
65/18.3	74/5.20	75/23.9	87/6.11	85/29.4	102/7.17	95/35.0	118/8.29	105/40.5	136/9.56
66/18.8	75/5.27	76/24.4	88/6.18	86/30.0	103/7.24	96/35.5	120/8.43	106/41.1	138/9.70
67/19.4	76/5.34	77/25.0	90/6.32	87/30.5	105/7.38	97/36.1	122/8.57	107/41.6	140/9.84
68/20.0	78/5.48	78/25.5	92/6.46	88/31.1	107/7.52	98/36.6	124/8.71	108/42.2	142/9.98
69/20.5	79/5.55	79/26.1	94/6.60	89/31.6	108/7.59	99/37.2	125/8.78	109/42.7	144/10.12
70/21.1	80/5.62	80/26.6	96/6.74	90/32.2	110/7.73	100/37.7	127/8.92	110/43.3	146/10.26
71/21.6	82/5.76	81/27.2	98/6.88	91/32.7	111/7.80	101/38.3	129/9.06	111/43.9	148/10.40
72/22.2	83/5.83	82/27.7	99/6.95	92/33.3	113/7.94	102/38.8	130/9.13	112/44.4	150/10.54
73/22.7	84/5.90	83/28.3	100/7.03	93/33.9	115/8.08	103/39.4	132/9.27	113/45.0	152/10.68
74/23.3	86/6.04	84/28.9	101/7.10	94/34.4	116/8.15	104/40.0	134/9.42	114/45.5	154/10.82

Fig. 5-5. Pressure and temperature chart for checking refrigerant container non-condensable gas content.

Why? Because the refrigerant (if there's any left) has to be recovered from the system anyway, and the system has to be opened up for repairs. Retrofitting the system to R-134a at this time would be less expensive than doing it later.

A simple retrofit generally should take about an hour and a half to two and a half hours. A more complicated retrofit that involves removing the compressor so it can be drained or replaced might add anywhere from 30 minutes up to 3 hours to the job depending on how difficult the compressor is to remove.

General Retrofit Procedure

The following guidelines are based on the SAE J 1661 standard which covers the recommended procedure for retrofitting an R-12 system to R-134a. Some vehicles may require more or less work depending on the application. Follow specific retrofit recommendations by the vehicle manufacturer.

Preliminary Inspection

Make sure the A/C system has not already been retrofitted to R-134a or charged with some other refrigerant. Talk to the customer and ask about any previous service that's been performed on the A/C system. Check the service fittings to see if R-134a adapters or some other type of service fittings have been installed. Look for a decal indicating the system has been converted or contains a different refrigerant.

Use a refrigerant identifier to positively establish that the A/C system you are about to convert contains only R-12. If a system is found to contain an unknown refrigerant, DO NOT connect your recovery and recycling machine to the vehicle. Be sure to use an identifier that also detects excessive noncondensable gases (air) in the system. Two to three percent air in a refrigerant charge will cause excessive head pressures and noisy

compressor operation.

Recover R-12 Refrigerant

If the system contains no refrigerant, this step is not necessary. If recovery is needed, follow the procedure mentioned previously in this chapter, using a UL-approved recovery and recycling machine to pull any R-12 and refrigerant oil out of the system.

Replace the Desiccant and Add Oil

This step is recommended whether the R-12 system already has a compatible desiccant (such as XH7) or not to restore the system's moisture protection. This is especially important on any retrofit that will use PAG oil.

Replace the accumulator or receiver/drier with one that contains XH7 or XH9 desiccant. Be sure to add the same amount of PAG or POE oil to the new unit as was in the old unit, or as specified by the vehicle manufacturer.

Replace Other Components As Needed

Though additional component replacement is usually not required in most retrofits, it may be necessary in certain applications.

Existing hoses and seals should not need to be replaced unless they are leaking or damaged. If hoses need to be replaced, install nylon barrier style hoses. If seals or O-rings need to be replaced, install ones made of Neoprene W or HNBR.

On some applications, a larger or more efficient condenser may be recommended to improve cooling performance with R-134a. A larger or auxiliary condenser fan may also be recommended. Condensers are expensive to replace, so the cost may only be justified if previous experience shows that a particular vehicle does not cool very well with a stock condenser.

Most compressors are compatible with R-134a and do not have to be replaced. But some do. Some compressors are also not rugged enough to handle the higher operating pressures of R-134a. Check for the manufacturers' specifications.

Install R-134a Service Fittings

Install the high and low-side adapters over the existing service fittings. The larger (16 mm) high-side adapter goes over the 3/8 inch threaded fitting on the liquid line, while the smaller (13 mm) low-side adapter goes over the 7/16 inch threaded fitting on the suction line.

If the adapters are the type that require removal of the **Schrader valve** cores from the original R-12 service fittings (many do not), then do so prior to installing the adapters.

Make sure the threads are clean before screwing the adapters on, and that the adapter threads have been treated with an anaerobic compound to lock them in place.

Install R-134a Retrofit Decal

Label the system so other technicians will know it contains R-134a and not R-12. The R-134a identification label, which is color coded light blue, should go over the old label (or remove the old R-12 label). The label should also be completely filled out (date of retrofit, type and amount of refrigerant, type and amount of lubricant used, etc.).

Also, remove any other decals, tags or references to R-12 on the vehicle.

Evacuate System

Evacuate the system at 29 in-Hg for a minimum of 30 minutes to remove all air and moisture. Dual evaporator systems should be evacuated for one hour.

Recharge with R-134a

Connect your charging equipment to the system, and charge the system to 80% of the original system capacity with R-134a. Then add additional refrigerant in 1/4 pound increments until the system is filled to about 85 to 90% of the original system capacity. Overcharging will reduce cooling efficiency and increase compressor discharge pressures excessively.

Confirm that the system is properly charged by observing the high and low-side pressure readings with a manifold gauge set. Do not use the sight glass (if one is provided) to determine the level of charge because the glass may appear cloudy even when the system is fully charged with R-134a and PAG oil.

Schrader Valve: A service valve that uses a spring-loaded pin and internal pressure to seal a port; depressing the pin will open the port.

1. A technician must be certified to perform all of the following A/C system services **EXCEPT**:
   a. Top off the refrigerant charge
   b. Check compressor clutch operation
   c. Recover and recycle refrigerant
   d. Identify the refrigerant type

2. A refrigerant recovery and recycling station must have a label saying it is:
   a. ASE-approved
   b. DOT-approved
   c. SAE-approved
   d. UL-approved

3. Refrigerant recycling equipment use and maintenance guidelines are defined in SAE Standard:
   a. J1989
   b. J1990
   c. J1991
   d. J1992

4. What color is a new container of R-134a?
   a. White
   b. Pink
   c. Blue
   d. Yellow

5. A container that may be used for recycled R-12 is stamped:
   a. DOT4BW
   b. DOT3BW
   c. DOT2BM
   d. DOT4MW

6. Before use, a container of recycled refrigerant must be tested for:
   a. Water contamination
   b. Non-condensable gases
   c. Chemical purity
   d. Oil contamination

7. Before testing recycled refrigerant, store the container in a warm location out of the sunlight for at least:
   a. 3 hours
   b. 6 hours
   c. 9 hours
   d. 12 hours

8. When recycling refrigerant, run the recycling pump:
   a. For at least one hour
   b. Until there are no bubbles in the sight glass
   c. Until the moisture indicator shows standards are met
   d. Until it automatically shuts off

Chapter One

AIR-CONDITIONING (A/C) SYSTEM DIAGNOSIS, TESTING, AND SERVICE *1*

Chapter Two

REFRIGERATION SYSTEM COMPONENT DIAGNOSIS AND REPAIR 17

Chapter Three

HEATING AND ENGINE COOLING SYSTEMS DIAGNOSIS AND REPAIR 30

Chapter Four

Chapter Five

This sample test can help you review your knowledge of this entire book. The format of the questions is similar to the certification tests given by the National Institute for Automotive Service Excellence. Generally, the questions here are more difficult than the programmed study questions you answered as you read the technical material in this book.

Read these review questions carefully, then read all the possible answers before making your decision. Always select the **best possible answer**. In some cases, you may think all the answers are partially correct, or you may feel that none is exactly right. But in every case, there is a **best** answer; that is the one you should select.

Answers to the questions in this sample test are found near the end of this book, following the glossary. If you answer at least 17 of these questions correctly, then you can be confident of your knowledge of the subjects covered in this book, and in the ASE Certification Test A7, Heating and Air-Conditioning. If you answer fewer than 17 correctly, you should reread the text and take another look at the illustrations. Also, check the glossary as you review the material.

1. The most likely cause of the A/C making a honking noise while operating would be:
   a. Compressor damage
   b. Drive belt wear
   c. Low refrigerant level
   d. Blower motor damage

2. Technician A says, bubbles visible in the sight glass of an R-12 system indicates a low refrigerant level.
   Technician B says, it is normal to see bubbles in the sight glass of an R-134a when the engine is running at a high throttle opening.
   Who is right?
   a. A only
   b. B only
   c. Both A and B
   d. Neither A nor B

3. To locate the source of a foul odor whenever the A/C system is operating, inspect the:
   a. Condenser
   b. Evaporator
   c. Compressor
   d. Receiver-drier

4. During normal operation, the receiver-drier on a TXV system should feel:
   a. Very hot
   b. Warm
   c. Cool
   d. Very cold

5. On a very humid day, you can expect A/C system pressures to be:
   a. Below the normal range
   b. At the low end of the normal range
   c. At the high end of the normal range
   d. Above the normal range

6. Technician A says, under normal operating conditions the line leading from the condenser to the expansion device on an A/C system should feel cold.
   Technician B says, a restriction in the A/C system low-side causes the line to feel cold.
   Who is right?
   a. A only
   b. B only
   c. Both A and B
   d. Neither A nor B

7. When an A/C system uses a suction throttling device, the device is typically located on the:
   a. Accumulator outlet
   b. Compressor outlet
   c. Evaporator outlet
   d. Condenser inlet

8. Which of the following is an expansion device?
   a. Fixed-orifice tube
   b. Pilot Operated Absolute (POA) valve
   c. Evaporator Pressure Regulator (EPR)
   d. Evaporator Temperature Regulator (ETR)

9. Technician A says, an A/C system with a low refrigerant level can cause low gauge readings on both the high-side and low-side.
   Technician B says, a defective expansion valve can cause a very low low-side pressure and normal to slightly low high-side pressure.
   Who is right?
   a. A only
   b. B only
   c. Both A and B
   d. Neither A nor B

10. What tool is used to locate a refrigerant leaks in an R-134a A/C system?
    a. Halide torch
    b. Electronic leak detector
    c. Refrigerant identifier
    d. Recovery and recycling station

11. Technician A says, Polyalkylene Glycol (PAG) refrigeration oil is used as original equipment on R-134a systems.
    Technician B says, store leftover PAG oil in a tightly sealed metal container for later use.
    Who is right?
    a. A only
    b. B only
    c. Both A and B
    d. Neither A nor B

12. Technician A says, discharging an A/C system slowly minimizes oil loss.
Technician B says, servicing an air conditioner involves discharging and evacuating the system until it holds a steady vacuum.
Who is right?
a. A only
b. B only
c. Both A and B
d. Neither A nor B

13. The fact that a cycling clutch compressor runs for only a short time, then turns off is most likely caused by:
a. A very low refrigerant level
b. A missing fixed-orifice expansion tube
c. An open compressor clutch circuit
d. A stuck over-pressure switch

14. Technician A says, a condenser corroded from acids formed by water contamination can be serviced by backflushing.
Technician B says, a chemical flush can be used to clean a corroded condenser.
Who is right?
a. A only
b. B only
c. Both A and B
d. Neither A nor B

15. The most likely cause of a heating system delivering too much heat to the passenger compartment would be:
a. Blocked outlet air ducts
b. Stuck-open blend door
c. Partial blockage of the heater core
d. Reduced current to blower motor

16. A gurgling sound from the radiator could mean:
a. Defective thermostat
b. Coolant contamination
c. Poor pressure cap seal
d. Radiator blockage

17. Technician A says, if there is no pressure drop for three minutes during a heater core pressure test, the heater core is not leaking.
Technician B says, the heater core is not contaminated with sediment if there is no pressure drop after three minutes.
Who is right?
a. A only
b. B only
c. Both A and B
d. Neither A nor B

18. Technician A says, if the heat level does not change when the temperature selector is moved on a vacuum-operated heating system the vacuum motor linkage may be disconnected.
Technician B says, no heat level change when the temperature selector is moved can be caused be a heater control valve malfunction.
Who is right?
a. A only
b. B only
c. Both A and B
d. Neither A nor B

19. When checking blower motor switch continuity:
a. Test points requiring continuity should read 0 ohms
b. Refer to a wiring diagram for specified voltage
c. Jump the blower motor switch to a known-good ground
d. Check switch amperage in each position

20. During the test for non-condensable gases in recycled R-12, the refrigerant must be:
a. At or above the specified pressure
b. Exactly at the specified pressure
c. At or below the specified pressure
d. Within 10 psi of the specified pressure

Actuator: A component that converts a vacuum or electrical signal into a physical movement, to operate a part such as a blend door or valve.

Ambient Temperature Sensor: An electronic device that transmits a variable voltage signal based on temperature. Sensor resistance varies with temperature changes.

Ambient Temperature: The temperature of the air surrounding a component.

Ambient Temperature Switch: A digital on/off device that senses ambient temperature and switches the compressor off when the temperature is too cold.

Blend Door: A door in a heating, ventilation, and A/C system that directs air through or around the heater core.

Chlorofluorocarbon (CFC): A chemical compound containing chlorine, fluorine, and carbon. When released into the atmosphere, the chlorine atoms detach from the CFC molecules causing a chemical reaction that turns ozone molecules into oxygen. Oxygen does not filter ultraviolet light as ozone does. R-12 (CCl2F2) is a CFC.

Coolant Temperature Sensor: Often designated as the Engine Coolant Temperature (ECT) Sensor. A variable resistance sensor threaded into the engine coolant passage. Changes resistance as temperature varies.

Coolant Temperature Switch: A digital on/off device that senses engine coolant temperature and switches off the A/C compressor when the temperature is too hot, reducing engine load.

Control Head: The dashboard-mounted unit that contains the controls for the heating, ventilation, and A/C system.

Cycling Clutch: A system that maintains refrigerant pressure by engaging and disengaging the electromagnetic compressor clutch.

Desiccant: A chemical agent in the receiver-drier of an A/C system used to remove moisture.

Expansion Tube: Also known as a fixed-orifice tube, this expansion device removes pressure from the refrigerant as it flows into the evaporator, but does not vary the flow rate.

Heater Control Valve: A cable, vacuum, or electric valve on the heater core inlet that controls the rate of coolant flow into the heater core.

Heater Core: A heat exchanger through which hot coolant flows and releases its heat by conduction into a passing air stream.

High-Side: The portion of the A/C system in which the refrigerant is under high pressure and at high temperature. It includes the compressor outlet, condenser, receiver-drier, and expansion device inlet.

Low-Side: The portion of the A/C system in which the refrigerant is under low pressure and at low temperature. It includes the expansion device outlet, evaporator, accumulator, and compressor inlet.

Schrader Valve: A service valve that uses a spring-loaded pin and internal pressure to seal a port; depressing the pin will open the port.

Thermostatic Bulb: A device that automatically responds to changes in temperature to actuate a damper in the air intake passage.

Thermostatic Expansion Valve (TXV): An expansion device that removes pressure from the refrigerant as it flows into the evaporator and also varies the refrigerant flow rate in relation to evaporator temperature.

Vacuum: A pressure less than atmospheric pressure.

Variable Orifice Expansion Tube: A type of expansion tube that varies the refrigerant flow rate to compensate for changes in compressor ouput.

Test Answers

Chapter 1 Review Questions

1. c, 2. c, 3. a, 4. d, 5. b, 6. d, 7. d, 8. b, 9. c, 10. a, 11. d, 12. a, 13. b, 14. d, 15. b

Chapter 2 Review Questions

1. c, 2. b, 3. c, 4. d, 5. a, 6. b, 7. a, 8. a, 9. c, 10. d

Chapter 3 Review Questions

1. a, 2. c, 3. d, 4. b, 5. a, 6. c, 7. b, 8. c

Chapter 4 Review Questions

1. b, 2. a, 3. a, 4. d, 5. c, 6. d, 7. b, 8. c, 9. a, 10. d

Chapter 5 Review Questions

1. b, 2. d, 3. b, 4. c, 5. a, 6. b, 7. d, 8. c

Sample Test Questions

1. c, 2. a, 3. b, 4. b, 5. c, 6. d, 7. c, 8. a, 9. c, 10. b, 11. a, 12. c, 13. a, 14. d, 15. b, 16. d, 17. a, 18. c, 19. a, 20. c

TEST PREPARATION NOTES